EARLY YEARS ACTIVITY CHEST

Science activities

CREDITS

British Library Cataloguing-in-Publication Data
A catalogue record for this book is available from the British Library.

ISBN 0 439 01734 3

ACKNOWLEDGEMENTS

The publishers gratefully acknowledge permission to reproduce the following copyright material:

Brenda Williams for 'Clothes to be seen in'; 'Tom's shadow' © 2001, Brenda Williams; Trevor Harvey for 'Watching and feeling'; 'How different?' © 2001, Trevor Harvey. All previously unpublished.

Every effort has been made to trace copyright holders and the publishers apologize for any inadvertent omissions.

AUTHORS
Alison Porter and Frazer Swift

EDITOR
Clare Miller

ASSISTANT EDITOR
Saveria Mezzana

SERIES DESIGNER
Lynne Joesbury

DESIGNER
Anna Oliwa

ILLUSTRATIONS
Anna Hopkins

COVER PHOTOGRAPH
Fiona Pragoff

Text © 2001 Alison Porter and Frazer Swift
© 2001 Scholastic Ltd
Designed using Adobe Pagemaker
Published by Scholastic Ltd, Villiers House,
Clarendon Avenue, Leamington Spa, Warwickshire CV32 5PR

Visit our website at www.scholastic.co.uk

234567890 234567890

CONTENTS

CONTENTS

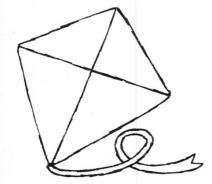

Introduction

This book provides a wide variety of fun, hands-on science activity ideas for the early years. The user-friendly approach aims to maximize flexibility and relevance to nurseries, reception classes and playgroups. All the activities, whether based indoors or outdoors, can be carried out using equipment and materials that will be familiar to all early years practitioners.

Science is all around us and to reflect this, the book takes six everyday themes – such as the kitchen, park and toy cupboard – as starting-points for the activities. The themes build on children's day-to-day experience and provide familiar, relevant contexts for science – essential if children are to develop positive attitudes toward science.

Curriculum links

The activities link to the Early Learning Goals for Knowledge and understanding of the world, and lead into National Curriculum Science at Key Stage 1. They aim to develop science skills and vocabulary, build on scientific knowledge and understanding, and encourage curiosity. In preparation for Key Stage 1, subjects introduced include forces and motion, light and sound, grouping and changing materials, life processes, humans and other animals, green plants, variation and classification and living things in their environment.

The activities cater for a range of learning styles and provide opportunities for individuals to explore using all their senses and to participate at their own level. Children are encouraged to plan investigations, co-operate, question, solve problems, take decisions, predict what might happen, obtain and record evidence, and evaluate and share their findings with others in a variety of ways.

Although science is the emphasis of the activities, these are essentially cross-curricular in their approach and provide links to other areas of learning in addition to Knowledge and understanding of the world: as well as offering many opportunities to develop literacy and numeracy skills, they include music, and art and craft work.

Getting the most out of activities

Some early years practitioners may find the idea of doing science with children a little daunting and can lack confidence in this area. However, it is important that they realize that they don't need to be 'experts' and

that many of the play-based activities that they organize on a daily basis already develop a range of science skills, such as observing, predicting, testing, recording and communicating ideas.

All the activities follow a step-by-step format which covers practical issues such as recommended group sizes and timings, the materials and equipment needed, and the preparation required. They also include suggestions for making the activities accessible for younger children and to extend them for older and more able children. Ways of involving parents and reinforcing the learning at home are also highlighted, along with multicultural links and basic background science where appropriate.

Photocopiable resources to support many of the activities are provided on pages 57 to 80. Recording is an important element of many of the activities, so use the photocopiable 'Recording sheet' on page 61 to encourage children to write about or draw pictures of what they did and what they found out. Computers could also be used to record investigations. It is important to encourage children to begin using scientific vocabulary as early as possible, and a set of photocopiable 'Key words' prompt cards (pages 62 and 63) are provided to help you do this. In planning the activities, remember:

■ Make safety your top priority – recognizing hazards and minimizing risks is an essential part of science, and children should be encouraged to do this at all times. The activities have been designed to be as safe as possible and health and safety advice is provided where appropriate.

■ The activities can be developed to meet the specific needs of your group – don't feel tied by them. You may wish to allow more or less time, to adapt ideas or do the activity at a different time of year. Allow children to repeat the same activity a number of times if they wish.

■ The process of 'doing' science is often more important than reaching a 'correct answer'.

■ Developing young children's self-confidence and curiosity through scientific activity is vital, so encourage them to explore and to put forward their own ideas. Different children will have formed different concepts in an attempt to make sense of the world around them, and it is important to acknowledge and value these, regardless of whether you consider them to be correct or not. The ideal is to help children challenge and develop their concepts through suitable activities.

▦ Try to use 'open' questions that allow for a range of possible answers and encourage discussion. Avoid 'closed' questions that require specific or 'yes' or 'no' answers. Ask children about their ideas, views and opinions and encourage them to discuss how they feel. The activities should not be seen as a test of knowledge, so phrase your questions carefully. For example, 'What do you think might be happening?' is much less threatening than 'What is happening?' and so reduces the fear of failure.

▦ If a child asks you a question that you can't answer, don't be tempted to make up a response. Try saying, 'Let's find out together' and use the situation positively for further investigations or research.

Links with home

The activities in this book have been structured around everyday situations to provide familiar starting-points for children, but these themes also enable follow-up and development at home.

Many everyday experiences are examples of science in action, and parents and carers can play a vital role in supporting the development of their children's scientific skills and concepts, and in fostering positive attitudes towards science.

Ask parents to encourage their children's curiosity and questioning, to listen to and value their scientific ideas, and highlight the benefits of finding time to have fun discovering things together. Stress that the process is more important than the content, and that they don't have to know all the answers.

The activities suggest ways in which learning can be reinforced at home by parents and carers. The families can also contribute by providing materials and resources for use in the activities, as well as by taking part in sessions to help you and the children with the chosen activity.

Getting organized for science

The environment in which early years science investigations takes place should be inviting, stimulating, comfortable and allow for exploration. It should encourage self-directed learning and should be organized in such a way that children can be independent and find the materials, equipment and tools that they need.

If possible, dedicate a part of the room to science activities and include space for displays of children's work and appropriate reference books, CD-ROMs and so on, so that children can carry out their own research. Provide

Keep safe in the park.

1) Never talk to strangers.

2) Never drop or touch litter.

3) Never touch dog poo.

4) Never go near water without an adult.

5) Never cross roads without an adult.

equipment and protective clothing for water-based and other messy activities. Store materials, equipment and tools in a logical, ordered way and make sure they are clearly labelled, using words and/or pictures. Recognition of the materials around them will enable the children to draw on resources more imaginatively and effectively when they are carrying out their investigations.

Many of the activities in this book make use of familiar materials such as yoghurt pots, cotton reels, kitchen-towel tubes, fabric remnants, straws, magazine photographs, food packaging and so on. Get into the habit of collecting these kinds of material and don't be afraid to ask parents to contribute.

Above all, the space should be safe. Keep small objects and dangerous materials and tools out of the children's reach. Involve them in identifying and agreeing simple, clear safety rules for using the space, and make sure everyone knows why the rules are needed. Make a list of these rules and display them where everyone can see them. Avoid clutter, keep things in good repair and always clear up at the end of an activity.

Science and the developing child

Children begin developing scientific skills from the moment they are born by using their senses to explore and make sense of their surroundings. In the early years, one of the key ways in which children learn is through play. All aspects of a child's development can benefit from scientific activity, from the social value of co-operation and discussion, to the creative development of ideas.

Young children are natural scientists. They are instinctively curious, keen to find out about their environment, and eager to use all their senses to physically interact with it. They observe, feel, smell, listen, compare, ask questions, investigate, experiment, try things out and weigh up evidence – all key science skills. The key to fostering and developing these skills is to make science fun and to base it on first-hand experiences in relevant contexts.

This chapter encourages children to investigate the scientific properties of foods and liquids in an accessible context. They will have the opportunity to test their sense of smell and to observe the effect of temperature on water and of heat on bread. Other inventive ideas show how to make science in the kitchen fun!

Science in the kitchen

GROUP SIZE
Six children.

TIMING
25 to 30 minutes.

HOME LINKS
Ask parents to discuss what happens to the level of water in the bath as children get in and out, and then when they take the plug out.

MULTICULTURAL LINKS
Discuss how important water is to us, for example, for drinking and growing crops. Introduce the fact that in some countries, people do not have enough clean water to drink or to grow plants to eat. Talk about the importance of not wasting water.

WATER WORKS

Learning objectives

To explore the behaviour of water and begin to think about relative volumes; to begin to use scientific vocabulary.

What you need

Large bowls of water or a water tray; tea strainers; colanders; jelly moulds; different-sized jugs; measuring jugs; water wheels and funnels; waterproof coats or aprons; cups or drinking containers (for teddy's use only); selection of teddy bears; food colouring.

Preparation

Ensure that the children have their sleeves rolled up, are not wearing watches and so on, and are wearing waterproof aprons or coats.

What to do

Discuss all the different ways we use water, for instance for drinking, cooking, washing, and even as ice and steam. Encourage the use of words associated with water, such as 'liquid', 'pouring' and 'wet'.

Encourage the children to explore the nature of water using a range of different containers in the water tray. Can they predict which one will contain the most water and think of ways to try this out? Ask them to predict how many times they will need to use a smaller container to fill a bigger one. Invite them to compare their results to establish the order of size ('smallest, bigger, biggest').

Have a teddy's tea party using cups of various sizes. Ask the children to match the biggest cup to the biggest bear and so on. After the tea party, ask them to check how much each cup contained using a measuring jug.

Support

Add washable food colouring to the water to make the water levels more visible. Reduce the number and variety of containers.

Extension

Introduce the idea of a fair test and encourage greater accuracy. For example, are the children always filling the container to the same mark? Are they spilling any water? Encourage older children to use measuring jugs and scales.

KEY FACTS
Water will always find its own level – it is pulled down by gravity and moves to the lowest point.

For health and safety reasons, water should be changed daily. However, explain to the children that they should never drink from the water play area.

UPS AND DOWNS

Learning objectives
To investigate which everyday objects float and which sink; to sort materials into groups; to encourage prediction and fair testing.

What you need
Water tray or bowls of water; spoons made of different materials such as wood, metal, plastic and clay; Plasticine; coloured foam or plastic numbers and letters; plastic containers with lids; towels; *Noah's Ark* by Lucy Cousins (Walker Books).

KEY FACTS
Objects made from 'heavy' materials that have a high density, such as metal and clay, will sink. Objects made from 'light' materials that have a low density, such as wood and plastic, will float. Density is a measure of the amount of matter ('stuff') in an object compared to its size.

Preparation
Make some Plasticine letters and numbers in various colours.

What to do
Read *Noah's Ark* with the children. Discuss the story and why it was necessary to build a boat. Look at the design of the boat. Place the spoons in the water – which float and which sink? Make two groups – one of 'sinkers' and one of 'floaters'. Put the plastic containers (with lids) in the water. Ask the children to predict what will happen. Will they float or sink? What happens if they take the lids off?

Ask the children to make a Plasticine ball – does this float or sink? Try changing its shape – can they make it float? (Try making a bowl shape.) Use this as a Noah's ark or alternatively, use a plastic tub. Make animals from Plasticine and load the boat two by two. Children can try to find the best way to balance the boat. What happens if the animals all stand on the same side? How many animals can they load onto the boat?

Support
Put some foam letters or numbers in the water. Do they float or sink? Do Plasticine letters or numbers float or sink? Ask children to retrieve 'floaters' or 'sinkers' by colour, letter or number.

Extension
Set a challenge of taking some treasure across the water to the other side. Use a 'sinker' such as a pebble painted gold as the treasure. Ask the children to make a boat from a range of materials – Plasticine, plastic bottles, pencils, straws, paper and string. Can they get the treasure across?

SMELL AND TASTE

Learning objective

To use all the senses to explore differences between foods and begin to classify them according to whether they are sweet, savoury and so on.

What you need

'Smell pots' made from yoghurt pots or film canisters with foil lids secured with elastic bands (make small holes in the foil to allow smells to escape) containing orange, mints, chocolate, onion, coffee and so on; taste samples such as small pieces of orange, cheese, apple, carrot, banana, chocolate, salt, and sugar-free soft mints; flip chart; *Billy's Beetle* by Mick Inkpen (Hodder).

Preparation

Before you do this activity, warn parents and carers and ask them about any allergies, intolerances or other dietary requirements that their children may have. Avoid nuts, and food containing nuts.

What to do

Enjoy the story *Billy's Beetle* with the children. Discuss how the 'sniffy dog' uses his sense of smell and how we use ours. Can the children describe any smells?

Warn children that they should not taste or smell things without checking with an adult first. Hands must be washed before sampling the foods. Pass around the 'smell' containers. Can the children identify the smells? Ask them to describe the smell, and write key words on a flip chart.

Ask children to close their eyes and to taste the food samples. Can they identify the food? Record the results on a chart. Which foods are easiest to identify? Encourage descriptive language and note it down.

Support

Ask children to identify food using all their senses, including sight. What does the food look, smell, taste and feel like?

Extension

Children could carry out a survey of the group to find out who likes/dislikes certain smells. Make a block graph of the findings.

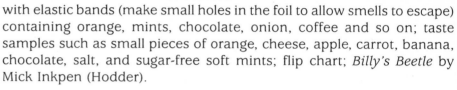

GROUP SIZE
Six children.

TIMING
30 minutes.

HOT, COLD AND WARM

Learning objectives

To use senses to explore differences in temperature; to use scientific vocabulary; to introduce health and safety in the home.

What you need

Three bowls of water (iced water, room temperature and warm); a range of objects for touching, for instance, woolly jumpers, wood, metal, polystyrene, marble slabs and so on; thermometer (use should be supervised); *One Snowy Night* by Nick Butterworth (Picture Lions); photocopiable sheet page 61.

Preparation

Prepare the bowls of water and set them up in an area where water spillage will not cause any damage. Make a copy of the photocopiable sheet for each child.

What to do

Read *One Snowy Night* and discuss with the children why the animals want to come into the house. Explore which objects feel warm or cold – metal and stone often feel cold, while wood and plastic surfaces are warmer. Ask the children to put their right hand on one object and their left hand on another, and to compare – does one feel warmer than the other?

Let the children take it in turn to put one hand in the iced water and one in the warm water. What do their hands feel like? Now take them out and put them both in the room temperature water. What do their hands feel like now? Encourage children to use their 'Recording sheets' to draw or write what they did during the activity and what they found out.

KEY FACTS
Some sense organs in the skin detect temperature, and others detect pressure and pain. Materials such as metals conduct heat away from your hand more quickly (they are *conductors*) so they feel cold to the touch. Other materials such as wool and plastic conduct heat away more slowly, so they feel warmer (they are *insulators*).

HOME LINKS
Children could look at clothes and sort them according to which is worn in hot, warm and cold weather. Alternatively, provide copies of the 'My house' photocopiable sheet on page 65 and mark 'hot spots', such as the cooker, iron and radiators, in red. Invite parents and carers to talk about the dangers of touching or getting too close to hot things.

MULTICULTURAL LINKS
Talk about the different climates around the world and how people's clothes and houses reflect the climate in which they live.

Support

Ask the children to put their hands in each bowl in turn in the following order: coldest, warmer, warmest. Engage a discussion about which feels the most and the least comfortable and why.

Extension

Use a thermometer to measure the temperature of the water in each bowl. Write down the temperatures. Repeat after about ten minutes. How have the temperatures changed?

ICE BALLOONS

Learning objectives

To explore the way in which water changes when it is cooled or warmed; to use scientific vocabulary.

What you need

A freezer; two balloons, one half-filled with cold water, one half-filled with frozen water; water tray; tea towel or pillowcase; bowl for holding wet balloons; a sink; scales; the photocopiable sheets on pages 62 and 63.

Preparation

Prepare the frozen balloon ahead of the session – it will need to be stored in the freezer overnight. Copy onto card the photocopiable sheets. Make individual word cards by cutting them out and use them to encourage scientific language during the activity.

What to do

Introduce the idea of balloons by discussing the times when the children have played with them. Start by showing the children an empty balloon and then half-fill it with cold water. Ask the children to hold the balloon and to describe how it feels. Is it how they expected? Let groups of children explore the water balloons, and encourage discussion.

Place the ice balloon in the water tray and let the children investigate and compare it with the water balloon. Encourage children to feel, see and hear differences between the balloons and to talk to each other about them. Use the science word cards to prompt the children's discussion. (**NB** If children handle the ice balloons out of the water, use a pillowcase or a tea towel to feel through.)

Ask the children to predict what would happen to the balloons on a hot day, or if they were left outside in the snow. If you have several ice balloons, they could predict and investigate what happens to them in various places – outside, in the fridge, on a radiator and so on.

Support

Let the children have some ice cubes to handle and melt in their hands.

Extension

Introduce the idea of warm and warmest, cool and coolest. Can children predict any changes in the weight of the balloons before and after freezing? Ask them to devise their own investigation and to record their results. Freeze water in an old margarine tub and notice volume changes on freezing and defrosting. (Children will need access to scales and a freezer.)

GROUP SIZE
Eight children.

TIMING
45 minutes; optional activity of 25 minutes the following day.

WHAT'S COOKING?

Learning objective
To investigate how some materials change when they are heated or cooled.

What you need
Bread; a cooker with a grill; chocolate; water; butter; cheese; ketchup; jam; access to fridge/freezer box; ice-cube tray; the science word cards from 'Ice balloons', page 13.

Preparation
Prepare small samples of food in advance in the ice-cube tray and put them in the freezer. Include water, butter, cheese, ketchup, chocolate, jam and any other appropriate foods.

What to do
Discuss breakfast that day. Ask how many children had toast and how they like to prepare it. Show the children some bread, pass it around and ask them to describe it. Use different types of bread if possible. Toast the bread. Discuss what has changed. Does it look, feel or smell different?

Show the children cold butter and put some on the toast. Wait for a few seconds. How does it change? Put a plate of hard, cold butter near a radiator or in the sunshine. Ask the children to check it every five minutes or so. Encourage the use of words such as 'hard', 'soft', 'melting' and 'hot'. Add cheese to the toast and heat it under the grill. Watch the cheese change.

During these activities, if you feel it is appropriate to taste any food, make sure children have clean hands and check for any allergies and dietary requirements. Don't forget to emphasize safety issues, and make sure children are supervised at all times.

Support
Ask children to make a foil shape or letter to put on top of the toast. They can then see where it has cooked and where it has not.

Extension
Show children the samples of different foods that you had stored in the freezer before the session. Ask children what they think the food samples are. Tip them onto a plate and notice what happens to them. Put them somewhere warm. Can the children predict what will happen to these frozen samples during the session? What do they feel and smell like? Record your findings. Use the science word cards to help describe what is happening.

HOME LINKS
Ask parents and carers to show their children how foods change during cooking at home, for instance, by showing examples of raw and cooked potato. Children could also mash the potato and explore how it changes.

MULTICULTURAL LINKS
Include foods and breads from other cultures and discuss festivals where lots of food is cooked to celebrate, such as Passover.

GROUP SIZE
Six children.

TIMING
40 minutes.

HOME LINKS
Ask parents and carers to provide food and/or packaging for this activity, and encourage them to discuss food during shopping, cooking and mealtimes.

MULTICULTURAL LINKS
Ensure that food samples from a range of cultures are included, and use pictures of foods being grown and harvested. Display a map of the world and mark on it where foods are grown. Talk about ways in which food is transported around the globe.

SETTING UP SHOP

Learning objective
To classify food according to similarities and differences.

What you need
Tinned, dried and salted food; fruit; vegetables; herbs and spices; large boxes to make into shelves and display cabinets; access to frozen food, or frozen food packaging; shopping bags; *Handa's Surprise* by Eileen Browne (Walker Books).

Preparation
Cut out and mount photographs and pictures of foods. Make space available for the shop area.

What to do
Introduce the activity by talking about what the children like to eat. Discuss where food comes from. Where do people's families shop and what types of food do they buy? Share the story of *Handa's Surprise* with the children. Show them a range of food and packaging, taking the things out of a shopping bag as if you had just bought them. Introduce the main food types.

Using the boxes for shelving, ask the children to display the items together as in a shop. Ask them to group the food by type: vegetables, fruit, cereals, rice, pasta, meat, fish and so on. Children could also display the food according to whether or not they need to be cooked, or where we store them and so on.

Ask some children to act as shopkeepers and encourage other children to visit the shop to buy food, asking for advice about how to store it, how to cook it and when to eat it.

Take care with small food samples (choking hazard) and food allergies (avoid nuts). Food for this activity is for handling and exploring, rather than eating.

Support
Younger children could group the food samples according to whether they like or dislike them, or by colour. They could also draw the food that they like the most from the selection.

Extension
Older children can look at food samples and discuss where they come from. Which are from plants and which are from animals?

GROUP SIZE
Six children.

TIMING
30 minutes.

HOME LINKS
Children could look out for ways in which people use mirrors around the home, at work or in the car. How many mirrors can they find at home?

MULTICULTURAL LINKS
Look out for stories, fabrics and paintings from a range of cultures that feature mirrors or shiny objects.

SHINY FACE

Learning objectives

To introduce the idea that some materials reflect light and some do not; to introduce scientific vocabulary.

What you need

A selection of shiny objects from the kitchen: metal spoons; pans; pan lids; bowls; colanders; baking trays; cups; tins; storage containers; templates of symmetrical shapes and letters; selection of other shiny objects, such as Christmas decorations, sweet-wrappers and sequins; different types of mirrors; paper; pencils; erasers; the photocopiable sheet on page 64; a copy of 'Snow White and the Seven Dwarfs' (Traditional).

Preparation

Prepare templates of letters and other shapes which are symmetrical. Try capital letters such as 'H', 'A', 'V', 'W', 'X' and circles, squares and triangles. Make a copy of the photocopiable sheet for each child.

What to do

Begin by reading the story of 'Snow White and the Seven Dwarfs' and talk about how the queen would look in her mirror. Use this to discuss mirrors and how people use them (for putting on make-up, brushing hair, shaving and so on).

Ask the children to explore the different objects and sort them into two groups: objects in which they can see their faces and objects in which they cannot. Discuss how the surfaces of shiny objects reflect light (light bounces off them), allowing us to see our reflections in them.

Look at reflections on the inside and outside of shiny spoons. Are they large, small, distorted, the right way up or upside down? Ask each child to draw what they see.

Use the 'Cat mask' photocopiable sheet. Children could add whiskers and colour the face. Help them to cut eye holes in the sheet and stick tin foil behind them. Look at the face in a dark area using a torch. Watch the eyes glow in the dark. Try other materials for the eyes and create different animal faces.

Support

Ask children to look at their reflections in ordinary mirrors and to describe their face to a friend, focusing on details such as the colour of their eyes and hair, the shape of their face, and whether their hair is long, short, straight or curly.

Extension

Use the mirrors with the templates. Hold the mirror over half of each shape or letter. Can the children predict what will happen? Children will see how they reflect. Can they draw some symmetrical shapes of their own?

KEY FACTS
We see objects because they give out or reflect light (light bounces off them), which enters our eyes. All objects, even black ones, reflect light to some extent, otherwise we would not be able to see them. Objects with shiny surfaces reflect light more than others.

Activities found here focus children's learning on the local and natural environment. There are opportunities to use all the senses to explore the area around your setting, suggestions for recording weather patterns over a period of time, and investigations into the use of different materials for some familiar items.

Science in the town

GROUP SIZE
Four children, each group with an adult.

TIMING
30 minutes.

LISTENING WALK

Learning objective
To use hearing and other senses to investigate the environment.

What you need
Tape recorder with microphone and tapes; magazine photographs for the display; flip chart; *Fergus the Farmyard Dog* by Tony Maddox (Piccadilly Press).

Preparation
Arrange for adults to take part in the activity (one adult per four children). Plan the route for the walk.

What to do
Ask the children to sit quietly. Explain that today they are going to close their eyes and listen carefully to the sounds around them. What can they hear? Note the sounds down on a flip chart.

Organize the children into small groups, each with an adult. Brief the children about road safety before the groups set off. The route should be planned so that it passes a range of places, such as shops, a park and a library. Stop in safe places and ask the children to listen out for birds, aeroplanes, helicopters, alarms, sirens, shoes, different footsteps, lawnmowers, cars accelerating and braking, bike bells, shouts, conversations, buses, lorries, wind and so on. After the walk, encourage children to think about the loudest and the quietest noises that they heard. Which were made by living things and which by machines? Note down their answers and make a display using magazine photographs of the different things heard.

Support
Read *Fergus the Farmyard Dog* and discuss the sounds featured in it. Which do the children recognize? Ask the children to help you make a list of sounds to listen out for on the walk.

Extension
Encourage older children to help you write a poem about the sounds heard, and ask them to try to imitate some of the noises.

KEY FACTS
Sounds are produced when objects vibrate, which causes sound waves to travel through the air. Our outer ear collects the sound waves and funnels them towards the middle ear where they hit the ear drum. This amplifies the sound and moves it through the inner ear. The auditory nerve takes the impulses to the brain where they are interpreted.

HOME LINKS
Let the children take home copies of the 'My house' photocopiable sheet on page 65. Ask them to note the different noises in each room of their house, to draw what makes the noise and to describe it.

BEACH DETECTIVE

Learning objective
To develop awareness of different environments and wildlife.

What you need
Magnifying glasses; treasure bags containing sand, a range of shells, driftwood, pebbles, pieces of chalk, dried seaweed, fossils, discarded fishing net, lobster pots and so on; *Bear's Adventure* by Benedict Blathwayt (Walker Books); fabrics and other materials such as cotton wool, sandpaper, velvet, bubble wrap and corrugated cardboard; an enlarged copy of the photocopiable sheet on page 59.

Preparation
Organize a trip to the beach if possible, with adequate helpers to ensure safety. If a trip to the beach is not possible, make up 'treasure bags' full of things from a beach for the children to investigate.

What to do
Read *Bear's Adventure* and discuss the story. Look at the things on the beach and use this to start the activity. What's near Bear on the beach?

Encourage the children to investigate the various aspects of life on the beach using all their senses to explore the environment. Provide magnifying glasses for the children to use for close observation. Compare beach pebbles with stones from the garden. Why are the pebbles rounded? Look for patterns on the shells. Are they rough or smooth? Do they have a partner or not? (Some are hinged, such as mussels.) Do any look like land snails? (Such as winkles.) Do any look like little hats? (Such as limpets.) Carry out some rubbings of the shells. Are any damaged? How might this have happened?

Make a touch-and-feel sea-shore collage, perhaps using sandpaper as the beach, bubble wrap as sea anemones, corrugated cardboard as shells and colourful velvet as fish.

Finish by displaying an enlarged copy of the poem 'Watching and feeling' and reading it aloud.

Support
Help prepare for the visit by looking and handling beach objects before the activity. Encourage the children to close their eyes and to describe what they feel.

Extension
Use natural objects collected from the beach for 'What am I?' feely boxes.

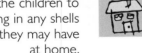

GROUP SIZE
Whole group.

TIMING
Introduction: 45 minutes, then 20 minutes daily.

HOME LINKS
Ask children to watch or listen to the weather forecast on television or on the radio and see if they can remember any of the symbols or words used. They can also look at weather charts in the newspaper with a parent or carer. Can children predict what the weather will be like tomorrow?

MULTICULTURAL LINKS
Use photographs or videos of extreme weather conditions to discuss the fact that different parts of the world have different climates. Which kind of climate would the children like to live in and why?

WEATHER WATCH

Learning objective
To observe and find out about features of the weather and to use different methods to record it.

What you need
Thermometer; paper or plastic party streamers (about 2cm wide); clear plastic bottle; *After the Storm* by Nick Butterworth (Picture Lions); ruler; stones; flip chart; adults to supervise outdoor activities.

Preparation
Cut the streamers into sections (about 50cm long). Cut the plastic bottle in half. Use the bottom half as a rainfall collector and the top half as a funnel inside. This prevents leaves from blowing in. Find a safe, protected place (out of direct sunlight) for the thermometer.

What to do
Read a book such as *After the Storm* and discuss the weather. Tell the children that over the next few days you will be observing the weather in different ways. Take the children outside and show them the thermometer. Ask them to notice where the marker is. Record the temperature on a flip chart each day.

Give each child a streamer to hold. Can they see or feel the wind? Ask them to look for signs of wind such as leaves moving, litter blowing about and so on. Firmly attach some streamers to a tree where they can blow freely. Which way are they blowing? Are they blowing a little or a lot? Record what you discover on a flip chart each day.

Select a place to put the rainfall collector and surround the bottle with stones to prevent it from falling over. Use a ruler to measure the amount of rain collected each day. Stress the importance of a fair test and ensure that the measuring equipment remains in the same place.

KEY FACTS
The term 'weather' describes conditions during short periods in a particular place, while 'climate' is the overall pattern of weather in a region. Weather and climate are governed by the sun – its heat creates wind and evaporates water from the sea to form clouds and rain.

Support
Observe the weather with the children and ask them to dress up one of their teddies in the appropriate clothing for the conditions.

Extension
Ask older children to make a weather chart, using symbols for each kind of weather, to record conditions each day. Invite them to present the weather conditions over a week as a block graph.

RAIN OR SHINE

Learning objective
To identify the materials used in different types of everyday clothes and why they were chosen.

What you need
Dressing-up clothes such as boots, umbrellas, sun-hats, scarves, woolly hats, rain coats, shorts, gloves, thick jumpers; copies of the photocopiable sheet on page 61; selection of shoes; water and dropper.

KEY FACTS
Children will compare the properties of materials. Emphasize the importance of waterproof clothing for wet weather, sun-hats for sunny days and warm insulating clothing for cold days.

Preparation
Collect or borrow a selection of children's clothes that reflect the four seasons.

What to do
Discuss the seasons and the different types of weather we associate with them. Relate this to the 'Tree collage' activity, page 33, in Chapter 4 and ask the children about other changes that might take place as we move from one season to another. What changes are we likely to see in the weather? This activity could also be run in parallel to the 'Weather watch' activity, page 19, in this chapter.

Put the clothes in the centre of the room and ask each group of children to select clothes for a given situation, such as a beach holiday, a game of snowballs, a walk in the park in the rain, and so on. Ensure that there are plenty of duplicates and emphasize the need to share and take turns. Dress up one person in each group and ask that person to 'parade' while the group explains their choice of clothes (for example, to keep them dry, warm or cool). Encourage the children to use science vocabulary when describing the materials used to make the clothes, and introduce the idea of materials having different properties.

Support
Introduce the activity by talking about the weather today and the types of clothes the children are wearing. Do the children feel hot, cold or just right? The activity could also be simplified by limiting the choice of clothing to different types of hats and footwear.

Extension
Ask children to investigate whether shoes are waterproof or not. Use a dropper to drop water onto different shoes. Watch what happens and decide which shoes are best for keeping feet dry. Has the water soaked in? Has it rolled off? Was it a fair test? Use the 'Recording sheet' photocopiable to record the results.

GROUP SIZE
Six children.

TIMING
40 minutes; vehicle parade: 30 minutes.

HOME LINKS
Invite the children to take home the 'Out of my window' photocopiable sheet on page 67 and draw which vehicles they can see from a window in their home at a given time. How many different types can they see? They could also complete the 'What's missing?' photocopiable sheet on page 68. Ask parents and carers to look at the pictures of types of transport with their children and spot what's missing.

ON THE MOVE

Learning objective
To observe vehicles closely, relating their design to their function.

What you need
A selection of vehicles such as bikes, trikes, scooters and pedal cars; space to ride; photographs of vehicles, or toy vehicles, with different wheels.

Preparation
Ask parents and carers to allow children to bring in bicycles, trikes, scooters or pedal cars for road-awareness training.

What to do
Start by singing the song 'The Wheels on the Bus'. Discuss bus rides and the kind of wheels that buses have. Compare these with wheels from other types of vehicles. Look at a bicycle together. Ask children if they can name the different parts. What are the surfaces of the tyres like? Why are the tyres like this? Why do they have air in them? Can they find the brakes? What do the brakes do? What might happen in the rain?

In groups, invite children to look at photographs of vehicles and toy vehicles. Ask them to look for similarities and differences, and to group the vehicles in different ways, for instance, by number of wheels, whether they carry passengers or goods, and so on. Emphasize road safety aspects as you discuss the vehicles.

To follow up the activity, organize a parade of the children riding their vehicles in a safe environment with adults. Some children could role-play pedestrians and pretend to be traffic-lights. Make a display of the parade with photographs of the children.

KEY FACTS
The activity provides opportunities to introduce forces (for example, pushes, pulls, and friction). Forces are very important in science: they are pushes or pulls that make things move, slow down, speed up, stop, change direction or change shape (by squashing, stretching, twisting and so on). Children can find it difficult to think about forces because they can't see them and sometimes they can't feel them either. Tyres have tread to increase grip (friction between the surface of the tyre and the road) and brakes also use friction (caused when two surfaces rub together).

Support
Concentrate on helping younger children to name the main parts of a bicycle and discuss what they do.

Extension
Older children could draw a bike and label the parts, or make rubbings of bike tyres and compare the patterns.

STICKS AND STONES

Learning objective
To identify different materials used to build dwellings throughout the world and to consider why they are chosen.

What you need
A copy of 'The Three Little Pigs' (Traditional); sticky paper; shoeboxes; old cereal packets; wallpaper and carpet samples; glue; fabric samples; felt; scissors; kitchen-towel tubes; paper and wax crayons; information books with clear pictures of buildings; photographs of different types of building.

Preparation
Gather images of different types of dwellings from around the world. Include skyscrapers, bungalows, igloos, tents, underground houses, houseboats and any other unusual homes.

What to do
Look at pictures of different buildings and point out the materials they are made from. Tell the story of 'The Three Little Pigs' and discuss the materials used in the different houses. Which house stayed standing? Why was this? Look at the outside of the building you are in and the dwellings around you. Ask the children to name some of the materials used and discuss why they are suitable. Why do we use bricks – are they hard or soft, strong or weak? Why do we have glass in the windows? Introduce the fact that glass is see-through (transparent) and waterproof. Why do we put tiles on the roof? Ask small groups to make one of the three little pigs' houses from a range of materials. Can they suggest ways to test their building? Are they able to blow it down?

Support
Raise younger children's awareness of the different parts of a house, such as the walls, roof, doors and windows.

Extension
Go on a short materials walk, stopping to enable children to feel different building materials and to make rubbings using thick wax crayons.

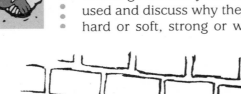

GROUP SIZE
Whole group to meet visitor, then groups of four to six children.

TIMING
Two sessions of 60 minutes.

CLOTHES FOR THE JOB

Learning objective

To investigate the idea that some people wear uniforms to protect themselves.

What you need

Photographs of uniforms with protective clothing (such as firefighters', police officers', builders', cricketers' and astronauts' uniforms); the photocopiable sheet on page 57; a copy of the photocopiable sheet on page 69 for each child; camera and film; a visitor whose work requires special clothing, such as a firefighter, a crossing patrol person or a police officer.

Preparation

Organize a time for your visitor wearing their uniform to come and speak to the children.

What to do

Start by reading the 'Clothes to be seen in' story to the children. Discuss the jobs and associated protective clothing. Before the visitor arrives, ask the children to think about what they might like to ask the visitor about their job and their uniform. Invite the visitor to talk about their work and how their clothing protects them. Give all the children a chance to ask questions. If there is a trying-on session, make sure you have a camera ready to record the experience.

After the event, ask the children to draw the uniform and write down one thing they found out about it. Make a display of their work and include the children's observations. For example, 'Sam thought that the helmet was heavy', 'Nasira thinks that the coat stops the flames', 'Rajesh says that the stripes can be seen in the dark'. Include photographs and make a 3-D display with borrowed items of uniform if possible. Provide each child with a copy of the 'Clothes for the job' photocopiable sheet and ask them to match the people at the top of the page to their hats at the bottom by drawing a line between each pair.

Support

Children could dress up and role-play being a firefighter or other uniformed worker. Encourage them to talk about their uniform and ask them to explain it to others in the way that the visitor did.

Extension

Older children could draw a firefighter or any other person wearing protective clothing, and label the special safety features of the uniform, briefly explaining what these are for.

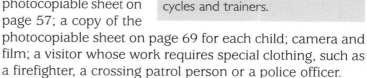

KEY FACTS

Hard hats are worn for several occupations and children may have their own cycle helmets. Pads worn by rollerbladers and cricketers are designed to spread out the force of an impact and prevent damage to the covered area. The materials are light and portable so the wearer can move easily. A firefighter has heatproof, non-flammable clothes, and reflective stripes enable them to be seen more easily in dark, smoky places. Children may have their own reflectors on clothes, cycles and trainers.

HOME LINKS
Find examples of protective clothing at home such as apron, oven mitt, rubber gloves, cycle helmet and so on.

MULTICULTURAL LINKS
If possible, make a collection of photographs of uniforms from different countries, such as army and police officers' uniforms. How do the uniforms differ? How are they similar?

FEELING FRICTION

Learning objective
To introduce the concept of friction.

What you need
A selection of shoes with different soles, including those with lots of tread; gloves of different types; washing-up liquid; water; photographs of cars.

What to do
Look at photographs of cars. Can the children name any of the main parts of a car? Talk about the wheels. What is the rubber part of a wheel called? Can the children suggest why cars need tyres? Talk about the way the tyres grip the road to prevent the cars from skidding, and discuss how the tread on tyres helps them to grip. Explain that when two things rub together – like the tyres and the road – this causes something called friction.

Explain that the children can feel friction for themselves. Ask them to rub their hands together. What can they feel? Ask them to push their hands hard together. Does this make the rubbing easier or harder? Put a little water in between the children's hands – what difference does this make? Ask the children to look at the soles of each others' shoes – who has smooth soles and who has rough soles (with patterns or grooves)? Which type of sole would grip the pavement best?

Support
Ask the children to listen to the sound their hands make when they are rubbed together. Does the sound change when their hands are wet?

Extension
Repeat the hand-rubbing but use a little washing-up liquid instead of water – what difference does this make?

Ask the children to wear gloves made from different materials (wool, rubber, leather and so on) and to notice how this affects how easy or difficult it is for them to rub their hands together.

KEY FACTS
Friction is a force which slows down moving objects and is created when two surfaces rub together. The rougher the surfaces, the greater the friction. The children will be able to hear the surfaces of their hands rubbing together and feel the friction creating heat. Friction is reduced by wetting the children's hands with water or washing-up liquid because these are smoother than the surface of their hands.

Activities in this chapter use children's toys to communicate scientific concepts in a way that children will find accessible and fun. Ideas include investigating how sound is made using toy instruments, testing levels of friction with toy cars and having a 'magnetic race' with cut-out cars.

Science in the toy cupboard

GROUP SIZE
Six children.

TIMING
30 minutes.

SORTED!

Learning objectives
To use observational skills; to identify and group different materials.

What you need
A range of toys of different types, ensuring a wide range of materials, such as metal, rubber, fabric, plastic, wood and ceramic; magnets; 'Key words' prompt cards from 'Ice balloons', page 13.

Preparation
Ask the children to bring in one toy each. Make additional prompt cards if necessary (for example, colour words).

What to do
Provide each group with an assortment of about ten toys and ask the children to classify them in a number of different ways. For example, they could start by sorting toys of the same colour together.

Make further groupings: by appearance (for instance, wheeled or not, shiny or dull), by function (used for building or not), by size (fits into my hand or not), and so on. Children may also suggest their own groupings.

Talk about the range of materials from which the toys are made and discuss the different materials found around the room. Use the prompt cards to remind children of the correct words. Start by grouping the toys by material such as metal, plastic, wood and so on.

Finish the activity by asking each group to select one toy and describe it to the others, explaining what they found out about it from this exercise.

KEY FACTS
A material is the matter from which something is made. Different materials have different properties (characteristics or qualities). Properties include texture, transparency, hardness, brittleness, strength, flexibility and elasticity, whether they are magnetic or not, and whether they conduct heat or electricity or not.

Support
With younger children, concentrate on grouping by size and colour, but begin to introduce vocabulary relating to materials.

Extension
Invite older children to investigate the objects using a magnet. Ask them which items are attracted by the magnet. Encourage the children to group the objects according to whether or not the material from which they are made is magnetic. Ask the children to record their findings, either pictorially or using a simple chart.

HOME LINKS
The children could carry out a survey of their toys at home to find out which is the most common material used. They could also look for toys that are made from a range of materials. Can they find a toy made from three or more different materials?

GROUP SIZE
Four or five, each
group with an adult.

TIMING
45 minutes.

FEELS FAMILIAR

Learning objectives

To investigate objects using the sense of touch; to develop scientific vocabulary.

What you need

A selection of familiar toys in a range of sizes, materials and textures that are safe to handle; one pillowcase for each group.

KEY FACTS
Our skin contains millions of tiny sense cells, including touch receptors on our fingertips that allow us to feel different textures, pressure receptors that allow us to hold delicate objects without crushing them, and temperature receptors that allow us to feel the difference between hot and cold.

Preparation

Put together a collection of toys (say six per group) and invite parents and carers to help with the activity. Put the toys in boxes or bags so that the children can't see them.

What to do

Begin by discussing the fact that we usually use our eyes to identify things, but that the way things feel can also help us do this. Ask each adult to put one object inside the group's pillowcase. Each child then takes it in turns to put their hand into the 'feely bag' to feel the object. Can they describe it to the others? How big is it? Is it hard or soft? Is it heavy or light, warm or cold? Is it rough or smooth? Can they guess what it is? Ask them not to say what they think it is until each child has had a turn, then ask for suggestions before revealing the toy. Discuss some of the characteristics of the object, encouraging the children to be as descriptive as possible. Repeat with the rest of the toys.

Support

Help younger children to describe the toys' characteristics by offering prompts, and give clues about what each toy might be.

Extension

Play *Kim's Game* using the toys. Ask the children to look at them for a minute and then cover them up. How many toys can they remember and name? Try removing one of the toys. Can they say which one is missing? Repeat several times, letting each child in turn remove a toy.

HOME LINKS
Children could play
Kim's Game with
objects from
different rooms at
home. Instead of
removing one of the
objects, the adult
should substitute it
with an object from
a different room.
Can the child spot
which object is the
'odd one out'?

WHAT A NOISE!

Learning objectives

To differentiate between loud, quiet, low- and high-pitched sounds; to use listening skills; to find out about different types of instruments.

What you need

Toy musical instruments, one for each child; four hoops; four A4 sheets of card; a marker pen.

Preparation

Ask the children to bring in a toy instrument if they have one. Write each of the following words on a card: 'blow', 'shake', 'pluck', 'bang'.

What to do

In small groups, allow the children ten minutes or so to explore how to use a range of instruments and to observe the sounds that they make. As a whole group, make sure each child has a musical instrument. Ask them to play their instrument loudly, then quietly.

Introduce the idea of high-pitched and low-pitched sounds, using your voice to make the sounds. Now ask whose instrument makes high-pitched sounds, and whose makes low-pitched sounds. Ask the children in turn to demonstrate the sounds for the rest of the group.

Place the hoops on the floor and put one of the cards in each. Ask each child in turn to place their object into the hoop that describes how the instrument is played. Finish by playing the instruments again, this time changing the rhythm. Go slowly, then faster, then as fast as possible.

KEY FACTS

Sound is produced when an object vibrates. The vibrations create sound waves which reach our ear drums and make them vibrate. Our brain interprets the vibrations as sounds. Fast vibrations make a high-pitched sound and slow vibrations make a low-pitched sound. Bigger vibrations (for example, created by blowing or shaking harder) make louder sounds.

Support

Concentrate on loud and quiet sounds. Encourage the children to produce music that would help someone go to sleep, and then music that would wake somebody up. Which is easier?

Extension

Try grouping the instruments according to whether they make high- or low-pitched sounds. Listen to a recording of some music and ask the children if they can identify the different instruments involved. Invite them to describe the kinds of sounds they make.

GROUP SIZE
Four small groups, each with adult support.

TIMING
45 minutes.

MUSIC MAKER

Learning objective
To explore how sounds are made by making and playing simple musical instruments.

What you need
Plastic bottles; glass bottles; shoeboxes or baking tins; rubber bands; rice or lentils; plastic bowls; Cellophane; water; the photocopiable sheet on page 70.

Preparation
Collect the materials listed above and prepare a wet area for the bottle organ. Organize extra adult help for making the instruments.

What to do
Ask each group to make the following instruments:

Drum: Cover a plastic bowl with Cellophane. Make sure that it is stretched taut and secure it with a rubber band. Play the drum by tapping the surface with fingers or a stick.

Shaker: Put some dry rice or lentils into a plastic bottle. Screw on the lid. Shake the bottle in time to a rhythm.

Rubber-band guitar: Stretch some rubber bands lengthways around a shoe box or baking tin. Play the bands by plucking them.

Bottle organ: Collect five identical glass bottles. Nearly fill up the first bottle with water. Put less water in the next bottle and so on. The last bottle should have only a small amount of water in the bottom. Make notes by blowing gently across the tops of the bottles. Alternatively, the bottles can be played by tapping them gently with a beater.

HOME LINKS
Encourage parents and carers to listen to different kinds of music with their children and to discuss the types of instruments being used, how they are played and what kind of sounds they make.

Support
Provide the children with ready-made instruments and encourage them to explore how they are played and the kinds of sounds they make. Introduce words such as loud and quiet, high and low sounds. Photocopy the 'Musical instruments' sheet onto card and cut out the word and picture cards. Invite the children to sort the instruments according to how they are played.

Extension
Try using different materials in the shaker, different-thickness rubber bands, different-sized bowls and a greater number of glass bottles. Explore how these variations affect the sounds that the instruments produce. Children could also decorate their instruments. See 'What a noise!' on page 27 for further ideas.

TOY FARM

Learning objective

To find out about food that we eat and where it comes from.

What you need

Modelling clay; toy farm animals; photographs of cows, chickens, pigs and sheep; photographs of food products that come from farm animals (such as milk, eggs, cheese, yoghurt, sausages, ham, cooked chicken, lamb and beef).

Preparation

Collect the photographs of farm animals and of their related food products. Arrange a visit to a farm if possible.

What to do

Begin by inviting the children to play with the toy animals. Can they name them and make their noises? Ask the children to imagine that they are farmers. What would they need to do to look after the animals? (They might feed them, provide a safe home and give them medicine if they are ill.)

Look at the photographs of real farm animals and ask the children to answer questions about each one by looking closely at the picture. Ask questions such as, 'How many legs does it have?', 'Does it have fur?', 'Does it have wings?'. Visit a farm if possible and ask the farmer to talk to the children about how he or she cares for the animals.

In their groups, ask each child to make a toy farm animal from modelling clay (a different animal for each group – pig, sheep, cow and chicken). Encourage them to use the photographs as a guide. Use the animals to make a model farm.

Discuss why farmers keep farm animals. Explain that we need them for food. Look at photographs of food products and help the children to name the animals that they come from. Make a display using the children's farm animals and the pictures of associated products.

Support

Sing 'Old MacDonald' together, with the children making the noises of the animals their group has made.

Extension

Encourage older children to list different ways of using the various foods, such as eggs in cakes, milk in milkshakes, cheese on pizzas, meat in sausages and burgers, and so on.

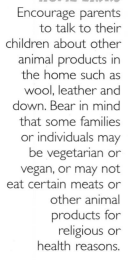

GROUP SIZE
Four children.

TIMING
60 minutes.

MODEL SOLUTION

Learning objectives
To use problem-solving skills; to co-operate as part of a group.

What you need
A selection of construction toys and toy figures; *The Lighthouse Keeper's Lunch*, by Ronda and David Armitage (Hippo Books); photographs or illustrations of boats, aeroplanes, hot air balloons, kites and bridges; string; a plastic coat hanger; paper and paints for the display.

Preparation
Place the construction toys in the centre of four tables for the children to work with. Prepare a suitable wall space for a display.

What to do
Read *The Lighthouse Keeper's Lunch*. Discuss how the lighthouse keeper's wife sent a basket from the cottage to the lighthouse, and focus on how the mechanism works.

Ask the children to imagine that they have the same problem but are not allowed to use a wire or a rope. How might they get the basket across the sea without getting it wet and without the gulls eating the food? Ask them to discuss it in their small groups and to make a model of their solution using the construction toys.

Ask each group to demonstrate and explain to the other children how they decided to solve the problem and how their solution would work. Encourage the other children to ask the group questions.

Make a *Lighthouse Keeper's Lunch* display using the children's models. Involve the children in painting a background scene showing the cottage and the lighthouse.

KEY FACTS
Use the activity as a starting-point to explore pulleys (using the story as the link), structures (bridges), floating and sinking (boats), and flight (aircraft, hot air balloons and kites).

HOME LINKS
Use *The Lighthouse Keeper's Lunch* to discuss different types of food and the importance of a balanced diet. Encourage parents and carers to discuss healthy eating with their children, and to help them keep a food diary over a week so that they can check how well they have eaten.

Support
Discuss possible solutions with the children, for example, a bridge, a boat, an aeroplane, a hot air balloon, a kite or even a catapult. Provide the children with photographs or illustrations of these to give them some ideas for their models.

Extension
Reconstruct the story by tightly holding a piece of string across the room and sliding a plastic coat hanger from one end to the other. Change the angle of the string and dicuss what difference this makes.

GROUP SIZE
Six children, each group with an adult.

TIMING
30 minutes.

GET A GRIP!

Learning objectives
To find out about friction; to investigate why friction happens and how it works.

What you need
A selection of toy cars; boards or trays (one per group); large sheets of sandpaper (one per group); paper; poster paints; wax crayons; old tyres.

Preparation
Invite parents and carers to help with the activity. Ask children to bring old toy cars. Prepare the room for the painting activity (see 'Support'). Arrange to borrow some old tyres from a local tyre retailer (see 'Extension').

KEY FACTS
Friction is a force which slows down moving objects and is created when two surfaces rub together. The rougher the surfaces, the greater the friction. The tread on tyres makes their surface rougher and so maximizes friction. A smooth or worn tyre will therefore provide less grip than a tyre with a good tread.

What to do
Ask the children to look at the tyres of toy cars. Are they rough or smooth? Ask if the tyres of real cars are rough or smooth. Can any of the children suggest why they have tread? Explain that this is to help the tyres grip the road to prevent them from skidding.

Invite the children to carry out an investigation in their groups. Using a smooth board or tray tipped at an angle, ask them to run the different toy cars down the board. Encourage them to start at the same point with two vehicles and to have a race. What happens? How might the tyres affect the results? Now use a large sheet of sandpaper on the slope. What difference does this make? Why might this be?

Support
Make colourful patterns by dipping the wheels of the toy cars into poster paints and by rolling them over the paper.

Extension
Arrange for a local tyre retailer to let you have some old tyres for the day. Encourage the children to feel the tread, and to compare its pattern and depth on different tyres. They could also make rubbings of tread patterns using white paper and wax crayons.

HOME LINKS
Suggest that parents and carers look with their children at different wheels and tyres on objects around the house (furniture, roller-skates, buggies, bicycles, toy trains) to compare their tread. How does this relate to their use? Is the tyre designed to maximize or minimize grip?

GROUP SIZE
Four children.

TIMING
30 minutes.

MAGNETIC RACE

KEY FACTS
A magnet is surrounded by an invisible force – a magnetic field. Magnets have a north and a south pole. Opposite poles attract each other and like poles repel each other.

Learning objective
To investigate magnets and observe the effect that they have on iron and steel.

What you need
Sheets of A4 paper; sheets of A3 stiff card; steel paper clips; small but strong magnets (enough for two per group); sticky tape; scissors; fridge magnets; toy trains with magnetic connectors.

Preparation
Draw a twisty track on a sheet of A3 card, with a start and a finish line. Make sure that the track is wide enough for the cars to pass each other. Draw the outline of two racing cars on the A4 paper and cut them out. They should be small enough to race on your track. Stick a paper clip underneath each car using a small piece of sticky tape.

What to do
Ask the children if they have ever seen magnets and where they saw them. Can any of the children say what is special about magnets? Hand out some fridge magnets and the toy train carriages and ask the children to explore them. What do they notice?

Give each group a race track, two cars and two magnets. Ask two children in each group to hold the card while the other two race the cars around the track by holding the magnets underneath the card (so that it attracts the paper clip) and then moving it along. Let the children swap roles when the race is finished.

Ask the whole group if anyone can suggest why the cars moved (because the magnets were attracting the metal paper clips). Explain that although magnets are not sticky, objects made of the metals iron and steel stick to them – they are 'attracted' to them. Show this by picking up some paper clips with one of the magnets.

HOME LINKS
Children could look out for and explore objects in the home that incorporate magnets, such as cupboard doors and fridge magnets. Provide magnets for them to test objects at home, and invite parents and carers to help them to make a list of things that are or are not magnetic.

Support
Ask the children to colour their cars and to draw people, buildings, trees and so on around their track.

Extension
Children could explore objects around the room with their magnets to see how many different things they can find that are attracted to the magnets. Can they predict which will be attracted and which will not?

This chapter looks at life cycles, growth and minibeasts by focusing on natural processes in familiar environments. There are ideas, amongst others, for growing plants from seeds, finding out about minibeasts on a nature walk and creating a garden in miniature.

Science in the garden

TREE COLLAGE

Learning objectives
To make observations about seasonal changes in nature; to collaborate as a group.

What you need
Collection of materials such as sandpaper, leaf templates, twigs, fabric, wool and tissue paper; large roll of paper; small boxes; pictures or photographs of trees at different times of the year; white paper; wax crayons.

Preparation
Draw a large tree shape on a roll of paper and attach it to the wall. Incorporate card 'treasure' boxes on the lower branches.

What to do
Go on a walk and point out the size, shape and colours of different types of trees. Encourage the children to touch the bark and leaves and to talk about the textures that they can feel. Look at pictures of trees in spring, summer, autumn and winter. Compare their shape and the colour of their leaves.

Make a collage of a tree using a range of materials. Arrange the children into four smaller groups, each representing a season, and give each group a part of the tree to work on. Incorporate a number of treasure boxes for children to display related treasures, such as leaves, conkers, feathers, blossom, toy birds and animals, and paper birds' nests. Make bark or leaf rubbings with wax crayons, and use them in the collage.

KEY FACTS
There are two types of tree: evergreens, such as holly and conifer trees, which stay green all the time; and deciduous trees, such as oak and horse chestnut, which lose their leaves in autumn and winter.

Support
Encourage the children to name the different parts of a tree (trunk, leaves, buds, flowers, fruits, bark, roots) and to label the collage.

Extension
Discuss the wildlife that lives in trees – birds, insects, bats, squirrels – and the uses of wood – for building, furniture and paper.

GROUP SIZE
Six children.

TIMING
45 minutes; investigation runs over seven days or more.

HOME LINKS
Encourage parents and carers to involve the children in gardening and to talk about plant growth. Children could also take the pots home and continue to look after their plants.

MULTICULTURAL LINKS

Use seeds from various parts of the world and look at photographs of the plants in their native environment. Edible plants would provide opportunities to talk about food from other parts of the world.

PLANT NEEDS

Learning objectives
To investigate what plants need to grow; to make predictions and carry out a fair test.

What you need
A yoghurt or margarine pot for each child; compost; large nail or knitting-needle; corkmat; watering can; mustard and cress seeds; labels; waterproof pen.

Preparation
Carefully make a hole in the bottom of the pots using a nail or a knitting-needle pushed through onto a corkmat. Fill with compost (about two thirds full). Prepare a pot for each child and label it with the child's name.

What to do
Encourage each child to put a pinch of mustard and cress seeds on their compost. Help them to cover this with a little more compost and gently firm it down. Arrange the children into three groups, each to carry out a different investigation:
- seeds in light with daily watering
- seeds in light, no watering
- seeds in cupboard (no light), with daily watering.

To ensure a fair test, make sure that all pots are identical with the same type and amount of compost and seeds, and that the pots are treated in the same way within each group.

Can the children predict what might happen in each group? Children should check their pots every day. After seven days, there will be a noticeable difference and children will be able to decide which plants they think look the healthiest.

KEY FACTS
Seeds need moisture, warmth and air in order to germinate. To grow, plants use energy from sunlight and water from the soil. They make their food from carbon dioxide in the air; this is called photosynthesis.

Support
Offer plenty of assistance in planting the seeds, and supervise the watering of the plants.

Extension
Plant sunflower seeds in pots. When they have germinated and the seedlings are about 4cm–5cm tall, transfer them outside to a protected sunny spot. Older children can then measure and record the plants' growth.

SOWING THE SEEDS

Learning objective
To be aware that there are different kinds of seeds and that seeds grow into plants.

What you need
A range of seeds such as beans, apple and orange pips, sunflower seeds, and avocado stones; 'flying' seeds such as sycamore or ash; spiky seeds like sweet chestnut or horse chestnut; dandelion heads with floating seeds; magnifying glasses; pictures of plants; whole fruit such as apples; seeded grapes; pea pods; avocados; knife (adult use); pictures of the plants from which the seeds originate; a version of 'Jack and the Beanstalk' (Traditional); the photocopiable sheet on page 71.

KEY FACTS
All flowering plants grow from seeds. Each seed contains a plant embryo and a store of food so that it can grow. A fruit is a seed container that protects the developing seeds until they are ready to be dispersed. Nuts are dry, hard fruits which contain one seed.

Preparation
Make sure that the grapes and peas are well washed.

What to do
Begin by telling the story of 'Jack and the Beanstalk'. Give each child a grape and a pea pod and ask them to break them open. How many seeds can they find inside?

Give the children a range of seeds. Ask them to work in groups and use their senses to identify differences and similarities in shape, colour, pattern, size and texture. Encourage them to use magnifying glasses to look more closely. Can they sort them into groups according to their appearance? Look at pictures of the relevant plants in magazines or books. (**NB** Take care not to use poisonous seeds and prevent children from putting seeds in their mouths, ears or noses. Do not use nuts in case of allergies and because of the possibility of choking if swallowed. Ensure that all the children wash their hands thoroughly at the end of the activity.)

Support
Ask if any of the children know what seeds are and what they grow into. Where have they seen seeds before? Show the children an apple and an avocado. Cut them open and look at the seeds or the stone inside.

Extension
Talk about the ways in which seeds are distributed, for example, by wind or animals, and relate this to the shape and size of the seeds. Give each child a copy of the 'Plant parts' photocopiable sheet, pre-cut into four separate parts: flower, stem, leaves, roots. Ask the children to put the parts back together to make a picture of a plant and see if they can name each part.

HOME LINKS
Ask parents to involve children in growing plants from seed and to give them responsibility for caring for the plants at home.

MULTICULTURAL LINKS
Talk about the countries from which apples, avocados, grapes, nuts and so on originate. Discuss the kind of climate some plants need to grow.

GROUP SIZE
Six children, each
group with an adult.

TIMING
45 minutes.

LET'S FIND MINIBEASTS!

Learning objectives

To develop observation and recording skills; to find out about a variety of minibeasts.

KEY FACTS
This activity provides an opportunity to introduce the idea that animals are suited to their environments (habitats) and to encourage respect for minibeasts and their homes.

What you need

Magnifying glasses; information books showing different types of minibeasts; A4 paper; coloured pencils; modelling clay; the photocopiable sheet on page 72.

Preparation

Select the areas you will visit and walk the route to get an idea of how long the activity will take. Include different types of environment, such as a grassy area, an overgrown area, brickwork and concrete.

What to do

Arrange the children in groups of six, each with an adult. Walk separately through the different environments looking for minibeasts. Children should observe (possibly using magnifying glasses), but should not handle the minibeasts. Adults could pick up minibeasts on a leaf or twig if necessary. Places to look include leaf litter, under old logs, rotting trees, on fences, in cracks in walls and on tree trunks. Give each child a copy of the 'Minibeast search' photocopiable recording sheet on which they can make a tick alongside the appropriate drawing every time they find a new minibeast.

After the walk, discuss the findings. How many different types of minibeasts did the children find? Which were the most common? Which animals moved quickly and which moved slowly? Which had the most legs? Look at the different characteristics (size, shape, colour) of minibeasts – what makes a spider different from a snail, or an ant different from a woodlouse? Where do the animals live: in the dark or light, wet or dry, underground or over ground?

HOME LINKS
Encourage parents and carers to observe minibeasts with their children and to carry out a survey of minibeasts in their garden or local area. Provide copies on card of the 'Minibeast jigsaw' photocopiable sheet on page 73 for parents and carers who would like to help their children cut out and do the puzzle.

Support

Look at a range of pictures of minibeasts at the beginning of the activity and ask the children to try to remember their names. Provide coloured pencils and paper for the children to draw the minibeasts, based on the pictures and their own observations.

Extension

Make a block graph showing each group's results. Which minibeast was the most common? Ask the children to make a minibeast from modelling clay based on their observations.

GROUP SIZE
Whole group.

TIMING
45 minutes, then
weekly checks.

HOME LINKS
Encourage parents
and carers to make
a 'minibeast-friendly
area' in their garden,
and ask the children
to share their
observations of it
with the rest of
the group.

CREATURE COMFORTS

Learning objectives
To find out about animals' homes; to develop respect for animals and their homes.

What you need
The Little House by the Sea by Benedict Blathwayt (Red Fox); *The RSPCA Guide to Garden Wildlife* by Val Porter (HarperCollins); old terracotta flowerpots; piece of old carpet; pieces of wood (preferably with bark); pictures of animals and their homes; the photocopiable sheet on page 74.

Preparation
Identify suitable places to make the animal homes; a quiet, partly-shaded grassy area is ideal. For useful information on attracting minibeasts, read *The RSPCA Guide to Garden Wildlife*.

What to do
Discuss the children's own homes and why we need homes – for example, to provide safety, shelter, comfort, somewhere to sleep, somewhere to play, and so on. Draw parallels with animals and their homes.

How many animal homes can the children name? Can they think of the name of a home for a rabbit, spider, bee or squirrel?

Involve the children in setting up minibeast homes by:
- putting some flowerpots on their side (to attract snails)
- laying a piece of carpet on the ground (to attract spiders, centipedes and worms)
- making a pile of old wood (to attract woodlice)

Check the homes every week to see what kinds of minibeasts are living there. Stress the importance of not disturbing the homes more than necessary and of not picking up the minibeasts.

Support
Read the story *The Little House by the Sea*. Discuss the different types of homes the animals found in the house and why they liked them.

Extension
Make a chart on which the children can draw pictures of the minibeasts they see. Give children copies of the 'Animal homes' photocopiable sheet and invite them to draw a line between each animal and its habitat.

KEY FACTS
Lots of minibeasts make their homes in places that are dark and damp (small bodies lose water quickly in hot sun), and that provide them with shelter from the weather and predators. Emphasize the importance of being kind to all animals, including minibeasts, and of treating animal homes with respect.

MINIATURE GARDEN

Learning objective
To encourage children to observe their environment and to take responsibility for living things.

What you need
For the garden: plants, such as mind-your-own-business, moss, saxifrages and herbs; seeds, such as alyssum, mustard or cress; gravel; pebbles; plastic mirror; old spoons and forks; potting compost; shells; pot or tray, approximately 30cm square and 10cm deep with drainage holes; a plastic figure; photographs or magazines showing different gardens; A4 paper; pencils. For the minibeasts: stones; twigs; acrylic paints and paintbrushes; thick thread or wool; PVA glue.

Preparation
Make a miniature garden and minibeasts in advance for the children to refer to. Try asking your local garden centre to donate plants, compost, trays and so on.

What to do
Encourage the children to think about gardens that they know. Ask them to think about planning a garden for a toy figure to enjoy. What would the little character want? Would they have an area to play or to sit in? Would they want a lawn and flower borders, or perhaps some trees? Or would they prefer a rockery, a pond or a vegetable plot? Ask them to plan their garden on paper and then decide together on a final design.

When they have planned the garden, ask children to fill the tray with compost. Use the plastic mirror to make a pond and create a path or a patio with the gravel. Using old spoons or forks, make small holes big enough for plants and roots. Firm around the base of the plants, and water these gently when all the work is complete. Encourage the children to take responsibility for caring for the plants.

Support
Prepare some paper templates of trees, plants, ponds, birds and so on for children to use for their garden planning.

Extension
Make giant minibeasts for the garden using pebbles, large beans or twigs. Paint the pebbles, cut thread for legs and antennae, and dip these in glue to stiffen them. Wait until they are dry, and stick them onto the painted pebbles.

LEAF PATTERNS

Learning objectives
To develop observation and classification skills; to raise awareness of the variety of leaves and flowers.

What you need
A variety of leaves and flowers (avoid flowers and plants which are poisonous or contain irritant fluids or hairs); magnifying glasses; paint; paper or card; self-adhesive transparent plastic.

Preparation
Prepare a collection of leaves and flowers for each group. Select a wide range of shapes and colours.

KEY FACTS
Leaves play a vital role in a plant's well-being. They capture light energy from the sun through a process called photosynthesis (see the 'Plant needs' activity, page 34). A green substance called chlorophyll in the cells of leaves captures the energy and creates food for the plant through chemical processes combining carbon dioxide from the air with water from the soil. Carbon dioxide is taken in from the air through tiny holes in the leaves (called stoma); these also give out oxygen.

What to do
Ask the children to investigate a selection of leaves using the magnifying glasses. Are both sides of the leaves the same? What are the differences? How do the shapes differ, or the edges of the leaves? How do their colours vary?

Now invite the children to group the leaves in different ways. Ask them if they can make a group of leaves which are round in shape (such as hazel or beech); spiky (such as holly or pine needles); look like a hand (such as horse chestnut or sycamore); or have a jagged edge (such as oak or hawthorn). Can they make up their own groupings, perhaps according to colour or texture? Repeat the activity with a selection of flowers, again looking at the number of petals, colours and so on. Be aware of any allergies to pollen.

Support
Encourage younger children to make picture prints using leaves. Use colours which reflect the season and the colours in the garden at the time: browns, yellows and reds in the autumn, and yellows, purples and blues in the spring.

Extension
Introduce the fact that the lines on a leaf are called veins. Invite the children to dry and press leaves and petals to make artwork such as greetings cards or bookmarks. Cover the cards with self-adhesive transparent plastic.

GROUP SIZE
Six children.

TIMING
30 minutes.

TREASURE HUNT

Learning objectives
To use and develop observational skills; to encourage exploration of shapes, colours, textures and smells.

What you need
Adult helpers; access to a garden; clipboards or pads; pens for adults.

Preparation
Brief adults and check the garden for potential dangers or hazards. Prepare a treasure hunt sheet listing the things the children must find, with a sketch of each item.

What to do
Discuss the idea of a treasure or an Easter egg hunt, or a game such as *Hunt the Thimble*. Ask the children to look for 'treasure' in the garden using their eyes, ears and their senses of touch and smell to find the various things on the list. The objects chosen would ideally fit in with other activities which you have already carried out, such as 'Let's find minibeasts!', page 36, or 'Leaf patterns', page 39. Use the activity as a way of reinforcing seasonal changes in the garden. Look for buds, seed heads, dead leaves and so on, depending on the time of year.

Emphasize that children should treat living things with respect and that minibeasts should not be handled or disturbed. Stress that the children should check with an adult before touching any unfamiliar items. The idea is not to collect each object, but to find it. Children should describe where it is to the adult within each group.

Try to include a range of living and non-living objects which have different features and properties. Children could be asked to find a flower which is pink, a leaf which is green, a scented flower, a spiky leaf, a snail, an ant, seeds, buds, bricks, smooth stones, painted wood and so on. Ensure that the children wash their hands thoroughly after the activity.

Support
Simplify the range of 'treasure' and provide clues for younger children. Use pictures of the treasure instead of words.

Extension
Ask older children to make their own short trail with clues such as 'I am brown and thin' or 'I can make my body wriggle and change length. What am I?'.

HOME LINKS
Invite parents and carers to organize a treasure hunt for their children at home, or to follow a treasure hunt that their children set up for them.

In this chapter, a favourite location is the source of scientific inspiration. Children will make kites to test air currents and the force of the wind, investigate life in a pond, use objects from a local park to make a natural feely book, and carry out many other imaginative activities.

Science in the park

GROUP SIZE
Whole group visit and then groups of six.

TIMING
Visit: 45 minutes; see-saw activity: 30 minutes.

HOME LINKS
Encourage parents and carers to discuss the weight of different foods with their children when cooking or shopping. The children could also think about the relative weight of members of their family. Who do they think is the heaviest? And the lightest?

TED WEIGHTS

Learning objectives
To describe movement and make predictions using scientific vocabulary; to investigate weight and balance.

What you need
A range of small teddies; six sets of see-saw balances; sticky labels; child-safe scissors; weighing scales; a copy of the photocopiable sheet on page 75 for each child; weighing scales.

Preparation
Arrange for parents to help with the park visit. Ask the children to bring in a small teddy or other soft toy.

What to do
Visit and use the playground at your local park. Talk about how the slide, swings, see-saw and roundabout work. Encourage the use of words such as 'push', 'pull' and 'balance'. Talk about movement and look for examples of things speeding up, slowing down or changing direction. Back at your setting, complete the 'Park play' photocopiable sheet together. Help the children to cut out the words and match them to the pictures.

Follow up the visit by asking the children to weigh their teddies or soft toys in the see-saw balances. Ask them to try different combinations of teddies. Can they predict which will balance and which will tip the scales? Can they explain why this happens? Talk about weight and the way that teddies of equal weight would balance.

Support
Use only a few teddies with clear differences in weight. Encourage the children to pick up the teddies and to compare how heavy they feel. Ask the children to use the terms 'lighter than' and 'heavier than'.

Extension
Encourage older children to weigh the teddies and to write each weight on a sticky label on the teddies' tummies. Ask the children to place the teddies in a line, lightest to heaviest. Explore the idea that the biggest is not always the heaviest and the smallest is not always the lightest.

KEY FACTS
The children will see a number of forces at work in the playground. Forces – pushes and pulls – make things speed up, slow down and change direction. Slides could also be used to introduce the idea of friction. The weight of an object is the force of gravity pulling it towards the centre of the Earth.

LIFT OFF!

Learning objective
To begin to know that forces are involved in enabling things to fly.

What you need
Tissue paper of various colours; thin straws; strong thread; glue; sticky tape.

Preparation
Bring in some real kites. Ask parents and carers to help with the activity. Cut some of the tissue paper into thin streamers to be used as tails for the kites. Cut enough 1m-long pieces of thread for each child.

What to do
Show the children two or three kites of different designs. Compare the sizes, shapes and colours of the kites. Ask the children if they have ever flown a kite in the park. What did it feel like? Could they feel the kite tugging at the string? What happened if the wind got stronger? And if it stopped blowing?

Ask the children to make their own mini kites using paper, straws and strong thread. Help the children to cut out the shape of the kite from the tissue paper and stick straws in a cross on the paper as support struts. Let them attach a tail on a corner of their kite and tie thread to the straws where they cross. Encourage them to use different shapes and colours.

Go outside and let the children 'fly' their kites. Discuss wind direction and encourage children to think about the best place to stand and the best direction to face. If there is no wind, they could run around holding the kite threads above their heads and letting the kites 'fly' behind them. Ask the children if they have any ideas about how kites fly. Do they know what it is that holds them up in the air?

Support
Make the kites in advance, but ask the children to decorate them. Alternatively, fly some real kites in the park and ask the children to describe what they see. Do some fly better than others? Can the children suggest why this might be?

Extension
Make some paper planes. Try different designs and decide which ones work best. Does the size of wings or the shape of the nose make any difference?

WIND IN THE SAILS

Learning objective
To investigate how sails work using scientific vocabulary.

What you need
Empty margarine tubs; modelling clay; aprons; pencils; sheets of stiff paper; child-safe scissors; bowls of water or water tray; photographs of sailing-boats; toy boats; adult helpers.

KEY FACTS
Sailing-boats are pushed along by the force of the wind in their sails – the stronger the wind the faster they can go. The force produced by the keel (the structure underneath the hull) stops the boat from being blown sideways.

Preparation
Ask the children to bring in empty margarine tubs. Prepare the room for a water activity and help the children to put on aprons and to roll up their sleeves.

What to do
Begin by asking the children if they know the story of Peter Pan and talking about Captain Hook's ship. Can they remember what it looked like? Was there anything special about it? Look at photographs of sailing-boats in books or magazines, and talk about the sails: the kind of materials from which they are made, their size, their shape, and whether they have pictures or patterns on them. Look closely at how the sails fill with wind. Ask the children to suggest what the sails are for and how they might help to push the boats along.

In their groups and with adult help, ask the children to make their own model sailing-boats using a margarine container as the hull. Help them to cut a sail shape from a sheet of stiff paper and to attach it to a pencil using sticky tape. Press a ball of modelling clay into the bottom of the container to stand the pencil in. The children can then sail their boats in the bowls of water. Ask them to blow into the sails to see if they can make the boats move. What happens if they blow harder or softer, or from a different direction?

Support
Make the boats in advance, or use toy sailing-boats. Role-play life on a sailing ship visiting new islands and sailing through stormy weather.

Extension
Ask older children to decorate their sails and to experiment with using different sizes, shapes and numbers of sails. What effect does this have? Discuss other ways in which boats are powered, for example, by poles, paddles and oars, but also by engines that turn propellers or paddle-wheels. Might the shape of the boat make any difference?

POND DIPPERS

Learning objectives

To find out about the range of living things in our environment; to encourage respect for living things.

What you need

Fine fishing nets; plastic trays (ideally white); paper and pencils; magnifying glasses; reference books.

Preparation

Get permission to do the activity from the owners of the park. Alternatively, you could use a local school pond, or a garden pond. Take a good supply of hand wipes and make sure that children wash their hands thoroughly after the activity. Brief the adult helpers about safety and make sure that no one drops litter in or around the pond.

What to do

Make a trip to a local pond. Arrange the children in groups of four, with one adult per group. Put some pond water in the trays. Ask the children to carefully scoop their net in the pond and to empty it into the tray. What can they see? Encourage them to use magnifying glasses to look as carefully as possible and to talk about what they see. Can they identify things as animals or plants? Do they know what kind of animals they are? What colour are they? Do they have legs, if so, how many? Have they got tails or fins? How do they move? Ask the children to draw some of the animals and plants that they found. Tell the children what they are called if you know.

Stress that the children must not touch the animals and emphasize the importance of returning them gently to the pond. Explain that the pond is the animals' home.

Support

Prepare younger children for the activity by looking at pictures of the kinds of animals and plants they might find. Use magnifying glasses to help the children see the pond life.

Extension

Use the children's drawings to inspire a pond-life mural or collage. Encourage the children to use reference books to identify some of the animals and plants that they found.

GROUP SIZE
Whole group then groups of five or six.

TIMING
45 minutes.

TUG OF WAR

Learning objectives
To understand that pushes and pulls are forces; to co-operate and make predictions.

What you need
The Rescue Party by Nick Butterworth (Picture Lions); a large strong rope; large plastic storage boxes (with flat bottoms).

Preparation
Tell parents and carers that you will be visiting the park, and ask for volunteers to help supervise the games that you will be playing. Plan the trip to coincide with dry weather.

What to do
Visit your local park and find a safe, flat, open area of grass. Sit the children on the grass and read them *The Rescue Party*. Discuss how Percy the park-keeper and all the animals pulled on the rope to rescue the rabbit down the well.

Organize a tug of war, with equal numbers of children on each side. Encourage the children to pull gently on the rope to begin with, and then to pull harder. Can they feel the other team pulling? What happens as a result of the pulling? Once the competition is over, invite one child to move from the winning side to the losing side. What difference will this make? Can the groups predict how many children will have to move to the losing side before it becomes the winner?

Split the children up into groups of five or six and hold a 'box race'. Ask one child in each group to sit in a box and the other four or five to push the box to the finish line.

Point out that the children have just been using pushes and pulls to move things. Explain that pushes and pulls are forces, and forces make things move.

Support
Just do the box race, but give the children the choice of whether they push or pull the boxes.

HOME LINKS
Children could look for examples of pushes and pulls around the home, such as pushing a vacuum cleaner, pulling a light cord, pushing a door bell or pulling kitchen paper from a roll.

Extension
Introduce the idea of friction by discussing the fact that as the bottom of the boxes rub against the grass, the force of friction makes them slow down. Try pushing the boxes on different surfaces. What difference does this make? Ask the children if they can think of ways of making the box easier to move (such as by attaching wheels to the bottom or sliding the box on ice).

GROUP SIZE
Whole group park visit then groups of four.

TIMING
Park visit, then activity: 60 minutes.

FEELY BOOK

Learning objectives
To use the sense of touch to explore different textures; to use scientific vocabulary.

KEY FACTS
Use the activity as a starting-point for looking at other properties of materials.

What you need
A selection of materials such as fabrics, foil, coloured card, wool, cotton wool, sandpaper, tissue paper, corrugated card, crêpe paper, feathers, bubble wrap, scourers, wire wool, sponge and string; paper; *In the Forest* by Maurice Pledger (*Maurice Pledger's Nature Trail* series, Templar Publishing); child-safe scissors; glue; 'Key words' cards from 'Ice balloons', page 13.

Preparation
Arrange a visit to your local park. Visit it in advance and plan a safe route for the texture trail. Identify stops on the trail and make a note of them. Ask parents and carers to accompany you for extra supervision.

What to do
Take the children on a texture trail at your local park. Make stops along the way and encourage the children to explore textures using touch. Ask them to try to find things that are rough, smooth, spiky, bumpy, sticky, dry, wet, soft, hard and so on. Make sure that the children wash their hands thoroughly afterwards.

Follow up the activity by reading *In the Forest*. Explain to the children that you would like them to make their own touch-and-feel book about their visit to the park.

Split the children into groups of four and ask each group to make one page of the book. Ask them to use the selection of materials to re-create some of the textures that they explored on the trail. They could also use them to represent people, birds, animals, rivers, ponds, buildings and anything else that they saw.

HOME LINKS
Choose a different texture each week and ask the children to bring in an object from home.

Support
Explore the textures of the materials before making the book. Sit the children in a large circle and put the materials in the middle. Ask each child to select (then replace) a piece of material in response to your instruction, which could be:
■ choose something that is rough
■ choose something that is spiky
■ choose something that is tickly
■ choose something that is soft.

Extension
Ask the children to include words on their pages that describe the textures, using the 'Key words' cards as a guide.

SAFETY FIRST

Learning objective
To be aware of dangers in parks and to identify ways of keeping safe.

What you need
Large sheets of paper; paints; paintbrushes; coloured pencils; glue; photographs of leaves and flowers.

Preparation
Arrange a visit to your local park and ask parents and carers to join you. Visit the park in advance to plan your route. Draw and cut out various leaf and flower shapes, enough for one per child.

What to do
At the park, split the children up into groups of six, with one adult per group. Walk around the route and ask the adults to talk to the children about dangers in the park. How many can they spot?

As a whole group, follow up the visit by discussing the dangers. How many did each group find? Reassure the children that parks are safe if we follow a few simple rules. Discuss each of the dangers in turn and ask the children to suggest a rule that would keep them safe. Make a list of rules and agree on the five most important ones. Paint these rules in bright colours on a large piece of paper to make a 'safety poster'. For example, your rules might be:

■ never talk to strangers
■ never drop or touch litter
■ never touch dog poo
■ never go near water without an adult
■ never cross roads without an adult.

Give your poster a heading such as 'Keeping safe in the park'. Provide each child with a leaf or flower shape and ask them to paint them in their choice of colour. Use these to decorate your poster.

Support
As a starting-point, talk about the kind of safety rules that children have in your setting. Provide photographs of leaves and flowers as a reference for the children's artwork.

Extension
Talk about the fact that some of the dangers to people, such as litter, broken glass and traffic, are also dangers to animals. Ask children to remind you of the safety rules you have and to think about what might happen if you didn't have them.

GROUP SIZE
Groups of six (with adult support).

TIMING
45 minutes.

HOME LINKS
Ask parents and carers to make the 'paper helicopters' from the photocopiable sheet on page 78 with their children. They should drop their 'helicopters' from a height, for example, over a banister or from standing carefully on a bed. The one that lands first wins the 'race'.

FREE FALL

Learning objectives
To begin to know about the idea of gravity; to make and test predictions.

What you need
A selection of natural things found in a park, for example, a stone, conker, acorn, twig, feather, leaf, sycamore seed; sheets of paper and metal trays; *The True Story of Humpty Dumpty* by Sarah Hayes (Walker Books).

Preparation
Either collect the objects yourself or organize a trip to the local park and collect the objects with the children. The activity itself could be carried out in the park on a still day.

What to do
Read *The True Story of Humpty Dumpty*. Talk about how the horse, the King's men and Humpty Dumpty all fell to the ground. Introduce the idea that this is because of something called gravity, which we can't see but which pulls everything down to the ground. Ask the children to stand and to jump up in the air on the count of three. Explain that they came back down because of gravity.

Organize the children into groups of six, each with a selection of objects (including a feather and a leaf). Ask one of the children to stand on stage blocks (or a similar secure surface) and to drop two of the objects (one in each hand, say a stone and a leaf). Emphasize the importance of letting the objects go at the same time and from the same height so that it is a fair test. Can the other children predict which object will hit the floor first? Try different objects. Explain that some hit the floor at the same time, while others (for instance, leaves and feathers) 'float' down more slowly.

KEY FACTS
The force of gravity pulls everything towards the centre of the Earth and gives objects their weight. The force of air resistance slows falling objects – objects with a greater surface area fall more slowly because there is greater air resistance.

Support
Concentrate on the fact that all things fall to the ground because of gravity.

Extension
Explain that the reason the feather and leaf fall more slowly is not just because they weigh less but also because they are flatter and more air can push up against them as they fall, slowing them down. Try making simple parachutes to illustrate this.

This chapter offers lots of exciting ideas to inspire children's scientific thinking through looking at themselves and the people and animals around them. Activities include identifying what pets need to stay healthy, looking at how people change as they get older, and focusing on seasonal changes through people's birthdays.

Science, my friends and me

GROUP SIZE
Pairs of children.

TIMING
40 minutes.

SPOT THE DIFFERENCE

Learning objective
To use observational skills and develop self-awareness.

What you need
Plastic mirrors; paper and coloured pencils; rulers; camera; the poem on the photocopiable sheet on page 60.

Preparation
Make a face template (see Support). Take photographs of all the children.

What to do
Begin by talking about the fact that we are all different and that no two people look exactly the same, and read the poem 'How different?'. Ask for two volunteers to stand in front of the group. Ask the children to spot similarities and differences between their faces, looking at features such as eye and hair colour, and whether their hair is long or short, straight or curly.

Ask each child to draw a self-portrait. Encourage them to look carefully at their faces in a mirror and to draw a head and shoulders portrait, including as much detail as they can. Encourage them to colour in their eyes and hair the appropriate colour, and to include any defining features such as freckles, missing teeth or hair decoration. Ensure that each portrait has the child's name on the front.

Now ask each child to choose a partner and to draw their portrait, colouring it in as before. Ask each child to compare their self-portrait with the portrait drawn by their partner. How are they the same? How do they differ? Make a display of pictures and photographs with names.

Support
Provide a face template for younger children to complete.

Extension
Choose a feature (for example, blue eyes) and make a 'block graph' on the wall by displaying the portraits that have this feature in a column. Repeat with another feature, such as curly hair or brown hair.

KEY FACTS
Our physical characteristics — such as our eye and hair colour — are determined by our genes. We inherit genes from our parents; half come from our mother and half from our father. We therefore inherit some of the characteristics of each parent.

Each gene controls a different characteristic, and each human cell contains between 50,000 and 100,000 genes. Many of our characteristics are modified by the way we live — for example, our height is influenced by our diet as well as our genes.

HOME LINKS
Children could draw portraits of members of their family or friends and look for similarities and differences. Remember to be sensitive to individual circumstances.

GROUP SIZE
Whole group.

TIMING
45 minutes.

PET ESSENTIALS

Learning objectives
To focus on what pets (and humans) need to be happy, healthy and safe; to develop respect for living things.

What you need
Soft-toy animals; picture books about pets; a copy of the 'What pets need' photocopiable sheet on page 79 for each child.

Preparation
Ask each child to bring in a soft-toy animal. You may like to arrange for a real pet to be brought in for the support activity. If you do, make sure that the animal is not put under unnecessary stress due to noise or handling, and check your local authority health and safety guidelines.

What to do
Ask the children to sit in a circle with their soft toys. Begin by asking the children how they care for their soft-toy animals. Ask them to imagine that the toys are real animals and to suggest things they would need to be happy, healthy and safe. Examples are food, water, sleep, exercise, company and a home.

Now look at pictures of pets in the books. Can the children name them? Do any of the children have pets at home? Can they think of anything else that pets need? Discuss what pets need, mentioning all of the things above, but also toys to play with, grooming and medical care (trips to the vet if they are ill or to prevent them from being ill). Stress the fact that having a pet is a big responsibility and that no one should get a pet unless they are able to care for it properly. Ask each child to complete the 'What pets need' photocopiable sheet.

Support
Arrange for a parent or someone from a local pet shop or animal welfare group to bring in a real pet for the group to look at. Encourage the children to ask the person questions about the animal and how they care for it.

Extension
Arrange a visit from your regional RSPCA Education Officer who will be able to speak to the group about caring for animals.

You could also talk about the fact that like pets, humans need food, water, exercise, sleep, company, a home and medical care to be happy and healthy. Ask the children if there is anything else that they couldn't live without!

HOME LINKS
Ask the children to find out about a family pet, or about a friend's pet, and its needs. Encourage parents and carers to involve their children in caring for pets on a daily basis (although children should not be given *responsibility* for this).

GROUP SIZE
Six children.

TIMING
45 minutes.

HOME LINKS
Provide children with the 'My house' photocopiable sheet on page 65 and ask them to draw all the light sources they can find at home in the appropriate rooms.

MULTICULTURAL LINKS
Display some examples or pictures of traditional puppets, including shadow puppets, from around the world and discuss their origins with the children.

ME AND MY SHADOW

Learning objective
To investigate shadows and how they are formed.

What you need
Torches; large sheets of white paper; sheets of coloured acetate; photocopiable sheets on pages 58 and 66; a selection of opaque, transparent and translucent objects (made of materials such as plastic, glass, Perspex, wood and metal); rulers; sticky tape; split pins.

Preparation
Plan to do the activity on a sunny day. Set up a 'screen' for each group using large sheets of white paper.

What to do
Read the story *Tom's Shadow* (page 58) to the children. Talk about day and night, light and dark, and light and shadows. Stress the importance of not looking directly at the sun or bright lights.

Organize children into groups of six. Ask each group to hold up their selection of transparent, translucent and opaque objects to their 'screen' and to shine a torch at each one in turn. Which make a shadow and which do not? Sort the objects into three piles – those that make shadows, those that do not and those that make very faint shadows.

KEY FACTS
Light is a form of energy. It travels in straight lines from a source (the sun, a flame or a light bulb). Shadows are caused when light is blocked out by an opaque object, or partially blocked by a translucent object.

Some objects are opaque (light is not able to pass through), some are transparent (light is able to pass through) and some are translucent (some light is able to pass through). Opaque objects form shadows but transparent objects do not. Translucent objects form faint shadows.

Support
Outside, ask children to look at their shadow and explain to them which direction the sun's light is coming from. Can they run away from their shadow? In pairs, ask the children to draw around their partner's shadow and to look at the shape.

Extension
Make shadow puppets by cutting out the 'Body' photocopiable sheet and by attaching a ruler with sticky tape. Use split pins to make 'hinges' for the arms and legs. Dance the puppets in front of the paper screen and try shining the torches through the coloured acetate. Can the children think of ways to make the arms and legs move?

GROWING UP

Learning objective
To think about how people change as they get older.

What you need
Paper; pencils; glue; magazine photographs of people of different ages; a camera.

Preparation
Ask a parent to bring their baby to visit the setting, and to bring bathtime equipment and toys. Prepare the children for the visitor and the baby. Ask them to think of questions that they could ask about the baby. Ask parents and carers to bring in photographs of their children when they were a baby and a toddler, and photocopy them. (If children do not have these, they could draw pictures of themselves instead.) Take a photograph of each child in the group. Collect magazine photographs of people of different ages. Make simple four-page books for each child.

What to do
When the visitor and the baby come to your setting, invite the children to watch the baby being bathed and playing with his or her toys. Encourage the children to ask their questions, and prompt them when necessary.

After the visit, discuss what sort of things the baby could and couldn't do. What can the children do that the baby can't? In groups, ask the children to each make a book about themselves as a baby, as a toddler and as they are now using their photographs (one page per photograph). Ask them to write their name and to draw their portrait on the cover. On the relevant pages, they should complete the sentences 'When I was a baby, I couldn't (walk)'; 'When I was a toddler, I couldn't (button my coat up)' and 'Now I am (five) years old, and I can (do both these things and I can count to ten!)'.

Support
Ask for photographs of the children as babies and use them to make a display. Add words that the children associate with babies, such as 'bottle', 'cry', 'buggy', 'nappy' and 'rattle'.

Extension
Ask older children to draw and name, in their books, two relatives or friends under the headings: 'older than me', 'the same age as me' and 'younger than me'. Look at photographs of people of different ages – can the children say who is older or younger? Discuss how people's faces change as they get older.

COLOUR CARNIVAL

Learning objective
To explore the relationship between colour and light.

What you need
Black sugar paper; coloured acetate sheets; sticky tape; child-safe scissors; bubble mixture and blowers; prism or sun-catcher crystal.

KEY FACTS
We often think of light as being white, but in fact it is a mixture of different colours (each having a different wavelength). We see objects in different colours because they absorb some wavelengths of light and reflect others.

When white light is shone through a prism, it is refracted and split into its component colours – red, orange, yellow, green, blue, indigo and violet. This is known as the spectrum of visible light.

Preparation
Arrange a visit to a local building that has stained-glass windows, such as a church, a temple or a mosque. Collect photographs of different cultural festivals, carnivals and celebrations. Ask the children to bring in objects, or wear something, of their favourite colour.

What to do
Look at pictures of different cultural carnivals, festivals and celebrations and discuss how colourful they are, focusing, for example, on the costumes and the fireworks. Visit the building and look at the windows from the outside and from the inside. Do they look different? Why might this be?

Follow up the visit by making a 'stained-glass window'. Organize the children into groups of four and give each group a sheet of black paper. Ask the children to cut out different geometric shapes. Stick different-coloured acetate sheets over the holes using sticky tape, overlapping some of the colours. Stick the sheets over a window. How many different colours can the children see? What has happened where the colours overlap? Why might this be?

Support
Group the children's objects according to their colour. Which are the most and the least popular colours? Use the objects as a starting-point for a display about colour in the world around us.

Extension
Ask the children if they have ever seen a rainbow. Can they name the different colours in a rainbow? Ask the children to make their own 'rainbows' by blowing bubbles outside. Can they see a colour spectrum on the surface of the bubbles? Hang the sun-catcher crystal or prism in the window and discuss the 'rainbows' on the walls.

GROUP SIZE
Whole group.

TIMING
60 minutes.

HOME LINKS
Encourage children to ask their family and friends when their birthdays are. Can they find a birthday for each season?

MULTICULTURAL LINKS
Find out about the ways in which different cultures celebrate birthdays. Discuss the fact that the seasons happen at different times of year in different parts of the world (Christmas is in summer in Australia).

BIRTHDAY SEASONS

Learning objective
To increase awareness of the months of the year and seasonal changes in nature.

What you need
Sheets of A4 white card; pencils; rubbers; paints; paintbrushes; photographs of natural changes through the seasons.

Preparation
Make a list of the children's birthdays from your records. Pre-fold the sheets of card to make a large 'birthday card' for each child. Ask parents and carers to help with the activity.

What to do
Introduce the activity by talking about birthdays. Can the children remember the month of their birthday? Or what the weather is usually like on their birthday? Introduce the idea of the different seasons and how nature changes. Look at some pictures of seasonal images. Link the seasons to the months of the year.

Divide the group into four 'season' groups according to their birthday months. Give each child a blank card and invite them to make a birthday card for themselves. Ask them to draw a picture of themselves on the front and to write their name and the month of their birthday underneath. Encourage them to paint, inside, a picture of something associated with their season (such as daffodils and baby birds in spring; ice-creams and sunshine in summer; falling leaves and squirrels collecting food in autumn; and bare trees and snowmen in winter).

Use the cards to make a 'Birthday seasons' frieze around the room incorporating the months of the year.

KEY FACTS
Seasons change as the Earth moves around the Sun. Because the Earth leans at an angle as it spins, one hemisphere gets more sunlight than the other (and so more heat) as it moves around the sun. The change in temperature causes the seasons.

Support
Make the frieze in advance using your photographs of seasonal images. Ask the children to draw or paint a picture of themselves and help them to stick it on the frieze under the month of their birthday.

Extension
Make a simple chart or block graph recording the number of birthdays in each month. Ask the children which month has the largest and which has the smallest number of birthdays.

GROUP SIZE
GROUP SIZE
Four children.

TIMING
60 minutes.

LOOKS TASTY!

Learning objective
To raise awareness of different types of food and what makes a healthy diet.

What you need
Modelling clay; small paper plates (one per group); pictures of different kinds of foods; a story-book about eating, such as *Oliver's Vegetables* by Vivian French (Hodder) or *The Very Hungry Caterpillar* by Eric Carle (Puffin Books); a copy of the photocopiable sheet on page 80 for each child.

KEY FACTS
We all need food to live – we eat in order to stay healthy, to enable our bodies to grow and repair themselves, and for energy. It is important to eat a balanced diet which provides all the nutrients we need.

Proteins are required for growth, carbohydrates and fatty foods give us energy, and fibre helps us digest the food that we eat. Many kinds of food – such as fruit, vegetables, milk and fish – also contain vitamins and minerals that keep our bodies working properly.

Preparation
Collect pictures of different food types and make a display that the children can refer to. Be sensitive to the fact that some children may be vegetarian or vegan, or may have special dietary requirements for medical, religious or cultural reasons.

What to do
Begin by reading a story-book about eating to the children. Discuss why we need to eat and ask the children if they can remember what they had for breakfast or lunch.

Talk about the fact that there are lots of different types of food, that we need to eat a balanced diet, and that we do this by eating a variety of foods. Introduce the children to the basic food types: proteins (meat, fish, milk, cheese, eggs, nuts and beans); carbohydrates (potatoes, rice, bread, pasta and fruit); fatty foods (oil, butter, cakes, chips and crisps) and fibre (wholemeal bread, fruit and vegetables).

Ask the children to work in groups and to make a pretend meal using modelling clay and a paper plate. Stress that they should make a balanced meal containing one of each of the food types in the display. Ask one child in each group to talk to the rest of the children about their meal.

Give each child a copy of the 'My meal' photocopiable sheet and ask them to colour in five of the food items that they would choose to make a healthy meal.

Support
Encourage the children to role-play buying, cooking and eating the meal.

Extension
Carry out a survey of food likes and dislikes in the group. Which food type is the most popular? Which is the least popular? Make a chart showing the results.

HOME LINKS
Parents and carers could help their child to keep a food diary of all the things that the child eats in one day.

MULTICULTURAL LINKS
Ensure that you use examples/pictures of foods from a wide range of cultures. Discuss with the children a typical day's food in a country such as India or China, and ask them to compare it with their own.

GROUP SIZE
Six children.

TIMING
60 minutes.

BODY BITS

Learning objective
To increase awareness of the parts of the body and how we use them.

What you need
A large roll of white paper (or the back of a roll of wallpaper); pencils; Blu-Tack; the photocopiable sheet on page 66.

Preparation
Cut two child-sized pieces of paper for each group. Ask parents to help with the groups. Be sensitive to the fact that some of the children, or some of their family or friends, may have physical disabilities, and be prepared to talk about this positively.

What to do
Begin by playing *Body I Spy* with the whole group. Challenge the children to spot parts of your body beginning with the letters A (arm, ankles), B (back, bottom), C (chin), E (ears, eyes, elbow), F (fingers, feet), H (head, hands, hair), K (knees, knuckles), L (leg), M (mouth), N (nose, neck), S (shoulders, stomach), T (toes, teeth) and W (wrist).

Organize the children into groups of six (with one adult per group) and ask one child in each group to lie on the white paper while the adult helps another child to draw around his or her body. Stick the body outline on the wall at child height.

Invite each child in turn to choose a body part and, with their eyes closed, to point to where they think it is on the body outline. How close did they get?

KEY FACTS
Two thirds of the human body are made up of water. Each of us has more than 50,000 million cells, each measuring about 0.025mm across. We have about 650 muscles and our skeleton consists of 206 bones.

HOME LINKS
Ask children to take the 'Body' photocopiable sheet home and to find examples of clothes for each body part (for instance, a hat for the head, shoes for the feet, trousers for the legs and gloves for the hands).

Support
Ask the children to complete the 'Body' photocopiable sheet and to name the different body parts. Sing the song 'Heads, Shoulders, Knees and Toes' and do the actions.

Extension
Ask a child to perform a number of simple actions, such as lifting a book, throwing a ball, jumping in the air and catching a beanbag. Can the other children name the body parts that the child is using to perform the actions?

Clothes to be seen in

Mr Jones the crossing patrol person put on his big yellow coat with the silver stripes and left the house to walk to school. It was a dark morning, and he was glad he had his coat. The silver stripes would show up in car headlights, so he knew he would be seen. Mr Jones smiled to himself and thought how different it had been when he was a soldier, 'Then I wore a camouflage outfit so that I wouldn't be seen! – it's just the opposite now.'

He was just turning the corner into School Lane when he heard a terrible screeching of brakes, and a crashing noise. There was Nazir the paper boy, lying very still on the road near his bike, and a car driver was bending over him. 'I didn't see him,' the driver said. A passing jogger in his track suit and trainers came running up. 'I'll phone for an ambulance,' he said, and ran quickly to the phone box.

A police car and an ambulance soon arrived. Mr Jones noticed that the police and ambulance people wore their yellow coats too, over their dark blue uniforms.

But by now Nazir was sitting up. He seemed all right, but the ambulance crew took him to hospital just for a check-up. 'At least you were wearing your safety helmet, Nazir – that stopped you being badly hurt,' they said.

Mr Jones said he would look after Nazir's bike. He also told the police they could speak to Nazir's father Ahmet at the fire station where he was a firefighter.

At the hospital, a nurse in a blue uniform met Nazir and took him to see a lady doctor in a white coat.

'You're fine,' the doctor said. 'But remember to be seen next time you go out in the dark'.

'He will,' said Ahmet. 'He has special armbands, but he hadn't put them on.'

On their way home, Ahmet took Nazir into the fire station and showed him the protective coats the firefighters wore when tackling a blaze. 'Just wearing helmets isn't enough, Nazir, these coats protect us from the heat, and help us to be seen.' he said.

Nazir remembered that, and next time he went on his bike, he wore his special armbands too.

© Brenda Williams

Tom's shadow

Tom liked his shadow. On winter nights, standing in front of his bedside lamp, he would make it dance on the bedroom wall. Or make the shadows of his fingers quack like a duck, and bite at patterns on the wall paper.

Occasionally, Tom caught a glimpse of Shadow in different parts of the house. He always ran in front of him going down the stairs.

Once, he saw Shadow in the moonlight as they walked across the park from Grandma's at Christmas, but everything looked different. The swings, so friendly in daylight, were like weird monsters, and the trees were black and scary. Shadow had behaved strangely, especially when car headlights flashed past from the nearby road. In the darkest parts, he wasn't there at all. When Daddy shone his torch to show the way, Tom thought he saw Shadow's eyes shining underneath a bush, but Daddy said it was just a cat's eyes glowing in the dark.

But now it was summer, and Tom loved playing games with Shadow. When he rode his bike down the garden path, Shadow rode a bike too!

'Hey Shadow!' Tom would say, 'I can make you jump!' And sure enough, Shadow would copy him leaping upwards with his legs open wide. Tom thought he could make Shadow do anything.

But he couldn't! Shadow had tricks of his own! In the mornings, Shadow followed Tom as he ran down the path. 'Come in front of me, Shadow!' Tom would yell. But no, Shadow wouldn't.

Then, when Tom turned back towards the house for his bike, Shadow suddenly leapt in front.

Shadow had other tricks. Sometimes he disappeared altogether! Tom would spend ages looking for him behind the shed and then, when Tom gave up and walked away, he would pop out again!

And...Shadow could shrink! 'How do you do that?' asked Tom, when Shadow became really tiny just before lunch. But Shadow never spoke. The overhead sun went behind a cloud, and Shadow was gone.

Later, at bedtime, when Tom went out to collect his toys, the evening sun moved from behind the cloud and there was Shadow. But, he was enormous, like a giant!

I wish I could change into a giant like Shadow, thought Tom.

© Brenda Williams

Watching and feeling

It's Winter – and the sea looks cold.
This bench is rough – the wood is old.

The pebbles lying on the beach
Are smooth and round – but out of reach.

They look so dull, until the brine
Washes them and makes them shine.

It isn't warm enough to swim –
The clouds are out, the sun's gone in.

So we must sit and watch the tide
Race in – and all the pebbles hide.

The sun comes out – it's feeling brave –
Its light reflects upon each wave.

It's warmer now, but we stay on
This wooden bench, here on the Prom.

I wish we had a canvas chair
Down on the beach – it isn't fair!

For sand is great – the pleasure lingers
Of softness sliding through your fingers.

This bench feels hard. As 'special treats',.
Mum buys some lollies, drinks and sweets.

I choose a drink. (My lolly's horrid –
The wrapper's iced and frozen solid!)

Mum pulls the tab, inserts a straw;
The drink soon goes – there is no more!

I grasp the can and squeeze it tight –
It's dented now and looks a sight!

I eat some sweets – they're tough but chewy.
They stick to my teeth – and feel quite gooey!

The sun gets warmer, the waves less rough –
Can't eat more sweets, I've had enough!

My lolly's melted! What a bore!
I'll have to drink it – through a straw!

© Trevor Harvey

How different?

I like all my friends –
But it's puzzling me
Why each of my friends
Is so different from me!

Janice is tall
But Michael is small –
And I'm short and fat.
(I like being that!)

John's voice is soft
But Malik's is loud!
Grace plays on her own –
Jane likes a big crowd.

Ellie hates blue
But Vashti likes red.
Paul does what he's told –
Sam won't go to bed!

Rachid can draw,
Nadine loves to sing,
And Ruby feels pleased
To play on the swing.

Rema is five
And I am aged three –
But Chris, my best friend,
Is younger than me.

My birthday's in May,
With Jane's in December;
Dan has one in June
And Ruth in November.

Though each of my friends
Is so different from me –
I LIKE all my friends –
And my friends ALL LIKE ME!

© Trevor Harvey

Recording sheet

Name

Activity

What I did

What I found out

Key words 1

rough	smooth
hard	soft
hot	cold
warm	magnetic
light	heavy
dark	shadow
float	sink

Key words 2

metal	rubber
wood	liquid
glass	solid
plastic	gas
fabric	clay
force	friction
push	pull

Cat mask

My house

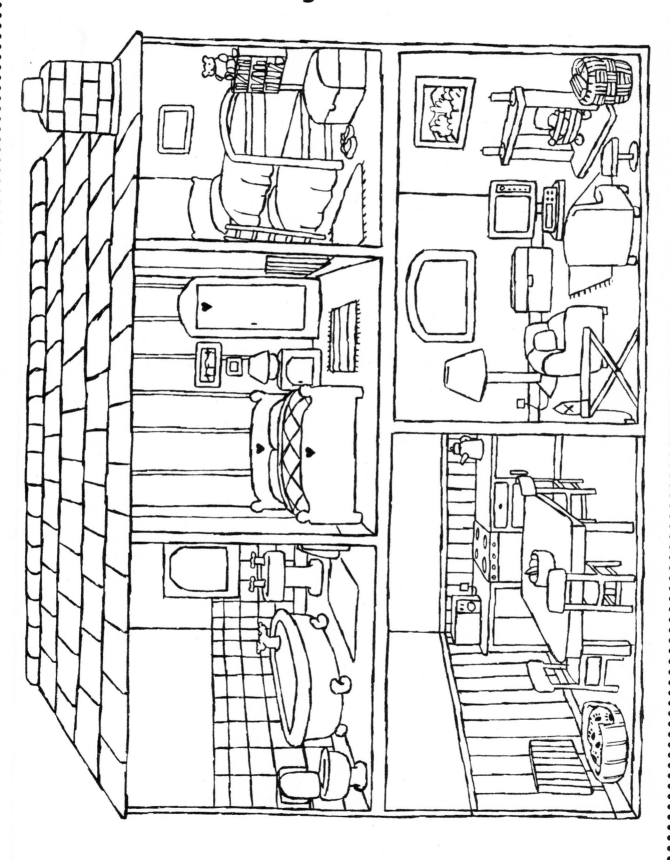

Body

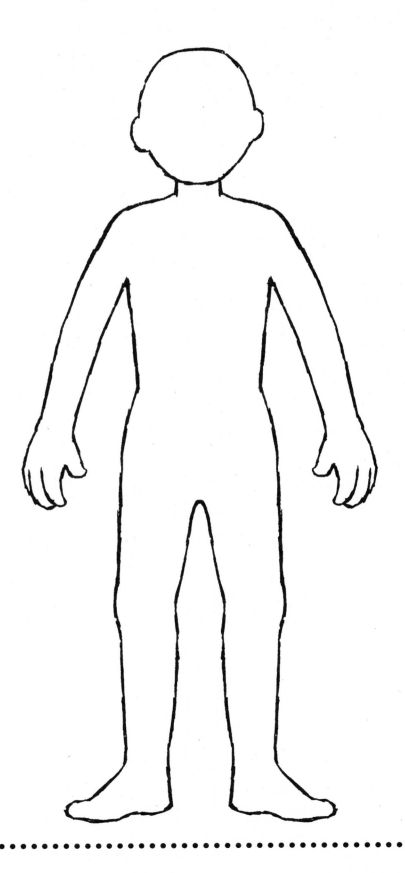

Out of my window

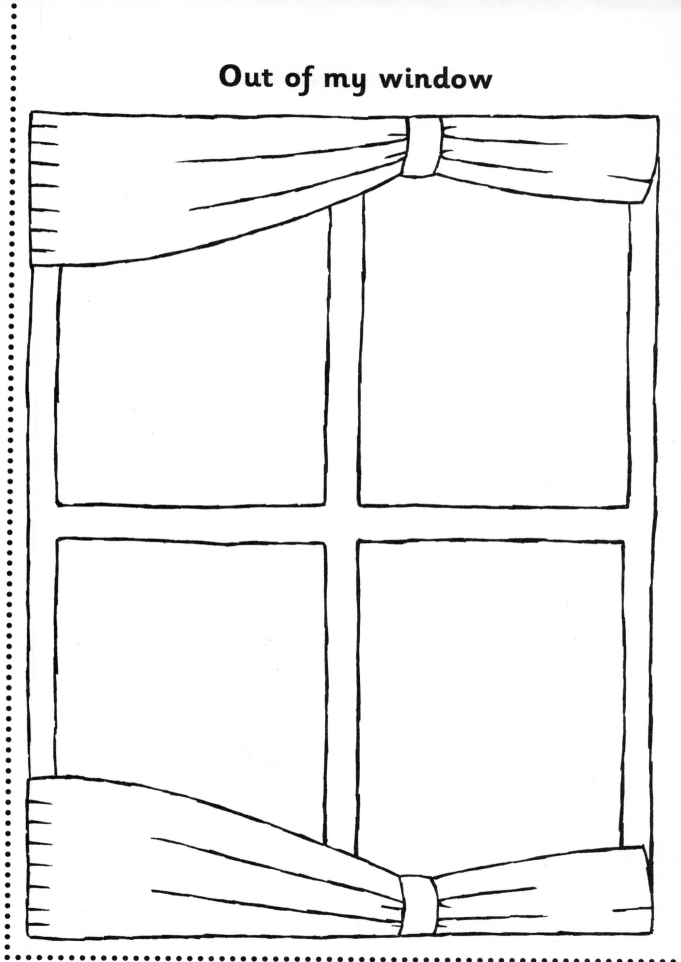

What's missing?

Clothes for the job

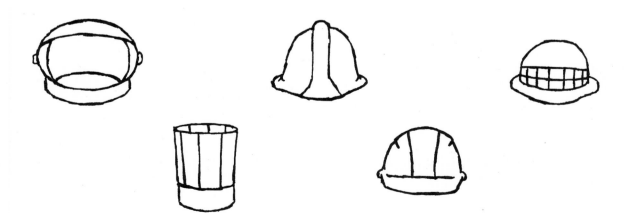

Musical instruments

pluck	blow
shake	bang

Plant parts

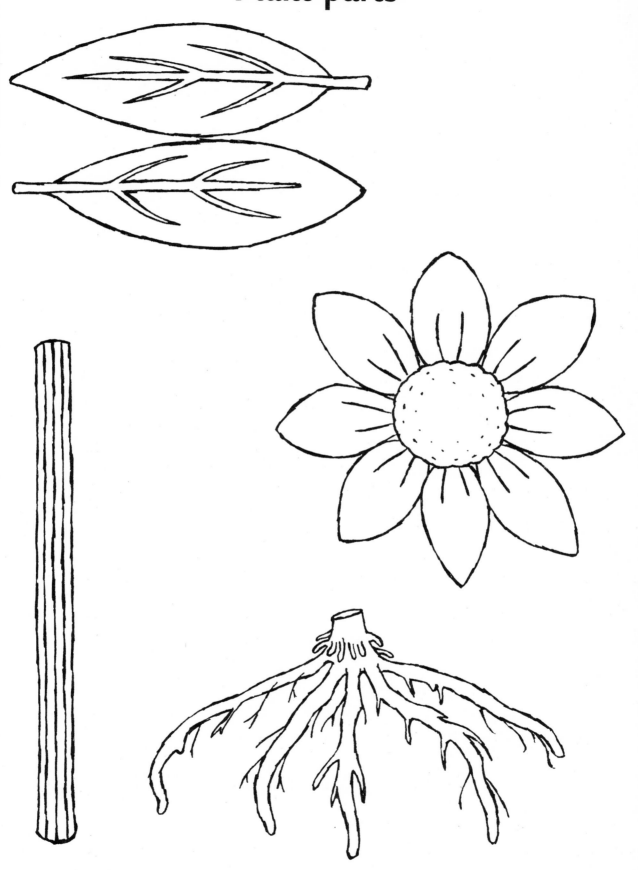

Minibeast search

Minibeast	1	2	3	4	5	6

Minibeast jigsaw

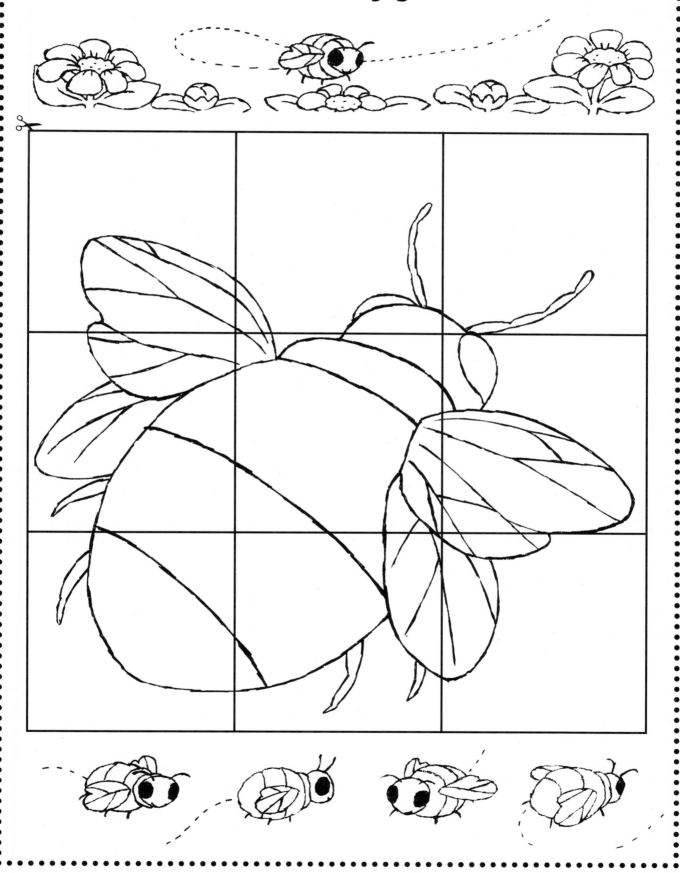

Animal homes

squirrel

den

rabbit

nest

fox

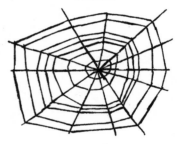

web

spider

drey

bird

burrow

Park play

push	pull
run	bounce
jump	climb

Flying things

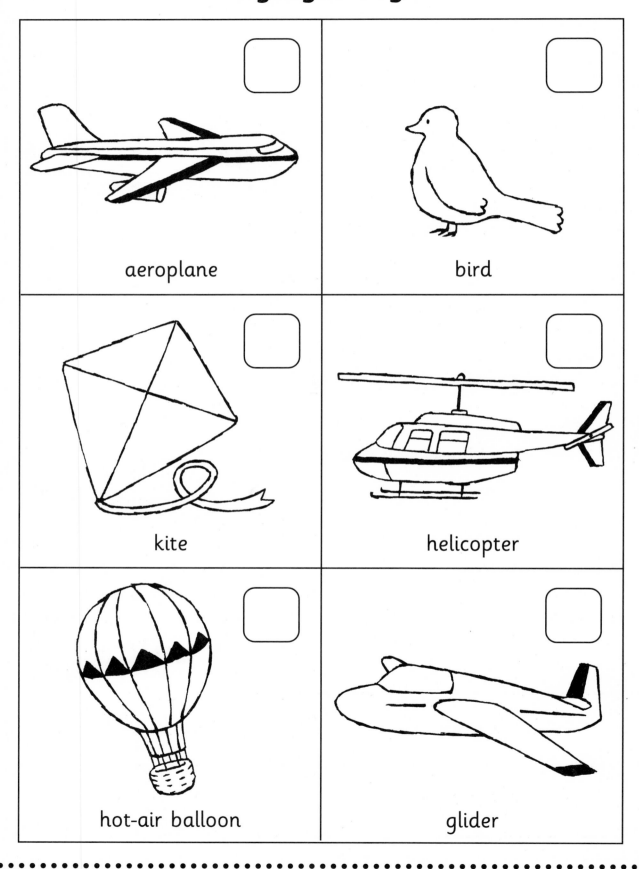

aeroplane

bird

kite

helicopter

hot-air balloon

glider

Spot the dangers

Paper helicopter

Cut out each rectangle below, cut along the dotted lines and attach paper clips to make two helicopters like this one.

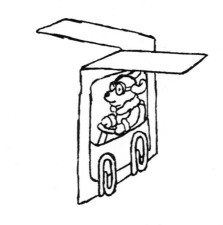

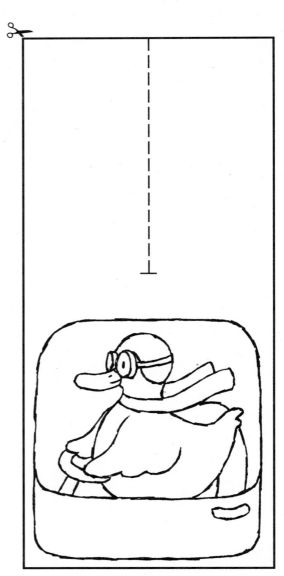